Best Young Adult Novels

VOCABULARY, ACTIVITIES, AND TESTS

Mary Rupe
Patricia Tarry-Stevens

 **J. Weston Walch, Publisher**
Portland, Maine

Users' Guide
to
Walch Reproducible Books

As part of our general effort to provide educational materials which are as practical and economical as possible, we have designated this publication a "reproducible book." The designation means that purchase of the book includes purchase of the right to limited reproduction of all pages on which this symbol appears:

Here is the basic Walch policy: We grant to individual purchasers of this book the right to make sufficient copies of reproducible pages for use by all students of a single teacher. This permission is limited to a single teacher, and does not apply to entire schools or school systems, so institutions purchasing the book should pass the permission on to a single teacher. Copying of the book or its parts for resale is prohibited.

Any questions regarding this policy or requests to purchase further reproduction rights should be addressed to:

Permissions Editor
J. Weston Walch, Publisher
P.O. Box 658
Portland, ME 04104-0658

—J. Weston Walch, Publisher

Cover illustration by Peter Gorski

1   2   3   4   5   6   7   8   9   10

ISBN 0-8251-2121-3

Copyright © 1992
J. Weston Walch, Publisher
P.O. Box 658 • Portland, Maine 04104-0658

Printed in the United States of America

DEDICATION

To our families: Don, Erin, Hal, Casey, and Kenna for their
understanding during the writing process and to Jean Tarry
for many types of encouragement and inspiration through
the years.

To the many outstanding reading educators at the University of
New Mexico and our colleagues in the Albuquerque Public
Schools who reaffirm and continually add new dimensions to
our teaching philosophies. Professors such as Zelda Maggart
and Virginia Resta are just some of the people who have
helped us through the years in our growing process.

—M. B. R.
—P. T.

Contents

Introduction to Young Adult Literature .... *vii*

Using the Book .... *x*

This thematic listing of the books covered in this volume indicates difficulty levels: **E = *Easy*, M = *Medium*,** and **D = *Difficult*.** (For further explanation of levels, read the section titled "Using the Book.") General topics are also given for each book.

Growing Up

A Day No Pigs Would Die (M) .... *Robert Newton Peck* .... Rural America 4–11

Are You There, God? It's Me, Margaret (E) .... *Judy Blume* .... Female adolescence 12–19

No Place for Me (E) .... *Barthe DeClements* .... Divorce, Witchcraft, Moving 20–26

The Sign of the Beaver (E) .... *Elizabeth George Speare* .... Native Americans, Colonial America 27–34

Family Problems/Special Relationships

Bridge to Terabithia (M) .... *Katherine Paterson* .... Childhood death, Friendship 36–43

Park's Quest (M) .... *Katherine Paterson* .... Vietnam War, Parental death 44–51

The Pinballs (E) .... *Betsy Byars* .... Child abuse 52–58

Sarah, Plain and Tall (E) .... *Patricia MacLachlan* ...... Prairie life 59–65

Sounder (M) .... *William Armstrong* .... Rural America, Prejudice 66–72

Special Challenges

The Crossing (E) .... *Gary Paulsen* .... Illegal aliens 74–81

Hatchet (M) .... *Gary Paulsen* .... Wilderness survival 82–89

Julie of the Wolves (M) .... *Jean Craighead George* .... Wilderness survival, Inuits 90–97

A Night Without Stars (E) .... *James Howe* .... Hospitalization, Physical deformity . 98–104

Mysteries

The Dollhouse Murders (M) .... *Betty Ren Wright* .... Murder 106–112

A Gift of Magic (E) .... *Lois Duncan* .... ESP, Divorce 113–120

The Indian in the Cupboard (E) .... *Lynne Reid Banks* .... Time travel 121–129

From the Mixed-Up Files of Mrs. Basil E. Frankweiler (D) .... *E. L. Konigsburg* .... Runaways 130–136

Fantasy/Science Fiction

The Green Book (E) .... *Jill Paton Walsh* .... Space travel, Colonization 138–144

Into the Dream (M) .... *William Sleator* .... ESP 145–151

The Phantom Tollbooth (D) .... *Norton Juster* .... Fantasy travel 152–161

Tuck Everlasting (M) .... *Natalie Babbitt* .... Eternal life 162–168

Historical Novels

Cave Under the City (M) .... *Harry Mazer* .... The Depression 170–177

The Devil's Arithmetic (D) .... *Jane Yolen* .... The Holocaust 178–185

A Family Apart (M) .... *Joan Lowery Nixon* .... The Orphan Train, 1860's 186–193

Number the Stars (M) .... *Lois Lowry* .... World War II 194–201

Appendix

Bibliography by Thematic Units (includes additional young adult novels) 205

Classics and Young Adult Literature 217

Additional Professional Reading 225

Introduction to Young Adult Literature

Why Teach Young Adult Literature?

The challenge to the language arts teacher in today's society is complex. Students exhibit a wide range of basic skills. Some are reading far below grade level, others have the necessary skills but are considered "aliterate" because they choose not to read, and still others are voracious readers. You will find a combination of these levels of readers in almost every classroom.

When you use books that are relevant to teenagers, more students are willing to take risks. They are interested and eager to involve themselves in reading. Higher thinking skills such as critical thinking, interpreting, analyzing, and predicting can be integral in the study of young adult literature. Margaret Early in 1960 summarized the three stages of reading growth as 1) primary (unconscious enjoyment)—infancy through beginning or middle years of elementary school, 2) secondary (egocentric years of adolescence)—late elementary through secondary years, and 3) aesthetic (creative reading). Many students at the secondary level will not read at the aesthetic level until their last years of high school. And a small minority will never reach the aesthetic level, even as adults. Unfortunately, many of our English class curricula are aimed at this level.

What implications does this have for the language arts teacher who has a prescribed curriculum to follow? The task for any teacher, whether in English, language arts, reading, special education, or many of the content areas becomes a question of how to motivate students, how to make them risk-takers, and how to involve them in the reading process. Arthea J. S. Reed in her book *Reaching Adolescents—The Young Adult Book and the School* summarizes this well: "This does not mean 'watering down' the content of the subject area; nor does it mean excluding the 'classics'; nor does it mean eliminating the basics; nor does it mean teaching only what interests the students today. It means bridging the gap between childhood and adulthood so that the content can be taught in a more sophisticated way."

Young adult literature lends itself easily to vocabulary study, characterization, and all levels of critical thinking. Sometimes young adult literature is the *only* bridge students have between problems of adolescence and potential growth, as a student and a human being. P. J. Petersen, author of *Would You Settle for Improbable?* and other young adult novels, said in a talk to teachers in Albuquerque, New Mexico, that the philosophy of reading young adult literature is that, for the young adult, this particular genre of literature provides perspective, comfort, and guidance. These books attract young adults because they tell them: "You are not alone."

The books chosen for this volume all have junior high-age protagonists. This does not mean that the books should or will be taught exclusively at seventh or eighth grade level. Many of these books will work well at high school level, such as *Hatchet* by Gary

Paulsen and *Sounder* by William H. Armstrong. Some of the books would work well in the upper elementary grades, such as *The Phantom Tollbooth* by Norton Juster and *Number the Stars* by Lois Lowry.

Young adult literature deserves much more credibility in our homes and classrooms. As in any other genre there are poor choices. But, for the most part, young adult books provide excellent models of literature. Authors such as Katherine Paterson, Irene Hunt, Robert Cormier, and Cynthia Voigt write beautiful literature that is relevant to *all* ages.

From our own personal perspective and classroom experiences (25 years total), our students became interested and more active readers when we introduced young adult books into our curricula. Parents also became more active as students brought home books and talked about them with their families. Conversely, we also heard teachers, administrators, and parents voice their concerns about the absence of the "classics." To these critics, we can point out that the same issues are discussed, whether it be Hawthorne's *The Scarlet Letter* or John Neufeld's *Sharelle*. Again, we see the young adult book as a possible bridge to the classics. (A list of classics and their young adult counterparts is given in the Appendix.)

Secondary students who say they've never read a book discover that being guided through the study of young adult literature in a classroom, with a book that is relevant to them, brings confidence and can even spark a love of reading.

Evolution of the Young Adult Novel

It would be difficult to pinpoint the actual beginning of the genre of young adult literature. Whether you would consider *Huckleberry Finn* or *Little Women* a young adult book would depend on your own criteria.

However, in the 1940's, Maureen Daly introduced a touch of realism in the book *Seventeenth Summer* (still read today). For the most part, though, young adult literature was typified by the Nancy Drew and Hardy Boys books. In the 1950's, books about cars, sports, and romance were popular, with such notables as *Hot Rod* by Henry Gregor Felsen and the Rosamond du Jardin books.

A new element of realism in young adult literature became noticeable in the 1960's with such books as *Mr. and Mrs. Bo Jo Jones* by Ann Head, *Island of the Blue Dolphins* by Scott O'Dell, and *The Contender* by Robert Lipsyte. By the 1970's, realistic young adult novels were the standard and continue to be so.

As our values and perspectives have changed, young adult literature has reflected those changes. Twenty years ago a teen would have been hard pressed to find a book on divorce or drug abuse. Today, a teen has not one choice, but many. Issues such as pregnancy, cocaine addiction, and even child abuse are topics now available in young adult literature.

Another example of the evolution of young adult literature is seen in the science fiction/fantasy categories. Thirty years ago science fiction fans had a steady diet of

Edgar Rice Burroughs and Robert Heinlein. Today, teens can enjoy Madeleine L'Engle, William Sleator, and Ursula Le Guin as well as the popular adult writers. In fact, a fantasy such as *The Lion, the Witch and the Wardrobe* by C. S. Lewis can be a wonderful introduction into the world of fantasy/science fiction and can entice even the most reluctant reader.

Young adult novels can be the catalyst for many topical units in the classroom. On an individual basis, these books can sometimes be cathartic. Issues in today's YA books can be highly relevant and correspond to the realistic needs and concerns of this age group.

Criteria for Choosing Young Adult Literature

Basically, all of the books included in this teaching guide follow three guidelines:

1. Written for the young adult audience.
2. A young adult is the protagonist.
3. Topics are aimed at the needs of young adults.

For reluctant or poor readers, we include some other cautionary criteria:

1. No time shifts.
2. Modern time setting.
3. No more than four to five main characters.
4. Lots of dialogue and action.
5. Able to be read within four weeks.

One important guideline for you to remember if you will teach a book to an entire class is to *like the book yourself*. If you specifically want to do a novel concerning changes in the family unit, for example, be sure to find one that you feel comfortable with and are excited about.

Teachers should also be risk-takers, however. A book that just seems "right" will minimize most of our cautions. For example, *The Lion, the Witch and the Wardrobe* by C. S. Lewis does not meet the listed criteria; however, this novel has been successfully used in secondary classrooms. Another example is *Where the Red Fern Grows* by Wilson Rawls. The beauty of such books is enough to sustain interest, no matter what guidelines the novel follows.

You might want to start your young adult book approach with students with a mystery. Especially with reluctant readers, the ones who complain they've never read a book (and seem to challenge anyone to make them), teenage mysteries such as *Killing Mr. Griffin* and *The Third Eye* by Lois Duncan can capture the attention of even the most recalcitrant.

Using the Book

Each book unit has the following:

- A Synopsis/Vocabulary page.
- A Student Worksheet for the first half of the book.
- A Student Worksheet for the second half of the book.
- A Final Test for students.
- Answer Keys for worksheets and tests.
- Extension Activities for students and teachers.
  (Chapter-by-chapter discussion questions are also included.)

Book units can be used in one of three ways: 1) teacher-guided study for an entire class, 2) independent study or, 3) in-depth committee or group study.

For your ease of usage, we point out the following features of the units:

1. If you will teach to an entire class, you can discuss vocabulary in detail. Additional assignments may be desirable, depending on your own students' mastery. We have found that mere dictionary definitions are confusing to students since many words have multiple meanings. Our particular method allows students to keep a vocabulary notebook. We present vocabulary words on the board and a definition among class members is discussed and recorded. Each student uses his or her vocabulary notes for worksheets, thereby ensuring better note-taking and organizational skills.

2. If a student reads the book independently, the final test and discussion questions would be sufficient to test comprehension. The final tests contain no vocabulary work.

3. On the worksheets, we have used a variety of question types. Multiple response questions are sometimes new to students and teachers. In these kinds of questions, students choose as many answers as are needed in order to complete the statement correctly. Students should be orally instructed to look for *all* the correct choices. Caution students not to confuse these kinds of questions with the more familiar multiple choice which are also used in the units.

4. In many of the Vocabulary sections, word lists are given for students to use. This is because of the extensive amount of vocabulary for that particular section. Other times, students will use the list of vocabulary words provided on the Synopsis page.

5. These exercises are meant as a springboard to other types of activities. In our own teaching we use Reader Response Journals, Reading–Writing Workshop, Jeopardy-type games as reviews on details, and play versions of many of the

chapters that have a lot of conversations. We have tried to include art, video, and drama ideas to expand the literature study.

Reading and Interest Levels

Reading and interest levels are a subjective matter. When students are interested in a subject matter, that enthusiasm will go beyond set reading levels. However, for your better understanding of our book units, we have assigned a general reading/interest level to each of the books in this anthology. Basically, this is what the categories mean:

EASY LEVEL   Easy vocabulary and/or
                        Easy concept for most middle school readers

MEDIUM LEVEL   Easy/Medium vocabulary and/or
                        Concept/story premise may be difficult for some

DIFFICULT LEVEL   Difficult or a lot of vocabulary and/or
                        A difficult concept for many middle school readers

Again, don't dismiss a book because we have labeled it "Difficult" or "Easy." Locale and time periods can be easy for some to envision, difficult for others. With most of the books in this unit it is very difficult to assign set levels. As always, use your own intuition and love of a book before considering reading levels.

Teacher and Student Materials for Book Units

GROWING UP

A Day No Pigs Would Die

by Robert Newton Peck

Synopsis

For Robert, living in the Shaker tradition on a poor Vermont farm in the 1920's, lessons for life come in subtle and unusual ways. His father, Haven Peck, is one of the best hog butchers in the state, but when the day comes when Robert's own pet pig must be slaughtered, it is a difficult step for both father and son. Even harder though is when Robert's father dies and 13-year-old Robert must take over and become a man.

Vocabulary

CHAPTER 1
1. foreleg
2. hunkered

CHAPTER 2
1. render
2. succotash
3. wince
4. provoke
5. carcass
6. pomade
7. goiter

CHAPTER 3
1. clergy
2. stout
3. frills
4. sow

CHAPTER 4
1. mirthful
2. pursuit
3. boar
4. mallet

CHAPTER 5
1. hanker
2. gumption
3. prosperous
4. sired
5. calico

CHAPTER 6
1. remedy
2. cornet
3. expulsion
4. tribulation

CHAPTER 7
1. nectar
2. talons
3. brood

CHAPTER 8
1. kin
2. desecrate
3. varmits

CHAPTER 9
1. quern

CHAPTER 10
1. Sabbath
2. perverts
3. shanty

CHAPTER 11
1. distress

CHAPTER 12
1. ailing
2. barren
3. fester
4. cipher
5. hearth

CHAPTER 13
1. sow
2. coaxed
3. husbandry
4. stewards
5. farrow

CHAPTER 14
NONE

CHAPTER 15
1. gilded
2. parcel
3. vespers

Name: _____ Date: _____

A Day No Pigs Would Die—Chapters 1–8

Character Identification: Write the character's letter in the blank next to each description of that character. You may use a letter more than once.

(a) Robert   (b) Haven Peck   (c) Mr. Tanner   (d) Robert's mother

1. _____ Helped Apron birth her calf.
2. _____ Gave Robert a piglet.
3. _____ Sewed up Robert's arm.
4. _____ Neighbor to the Pecks.
5. _____ Thought Abner Doubleday was more important than Ethan Allen.
6. _____ Owned Bob and Bib.
7. _____ Owned Pinky.
8. _____ Had to be tutored in English.
9. _____ Drove the wagon to where Mr. Hillman was digging up a grave.
10. _____ Talks a lot with Aunt Carrie.

Comprehension: Haven Peck was a man of few words but full of wisdom. Paraphrase, in your own words, what Haven Peck meant by each of these statements.

1. "Anything will bite, be it provoked." _____

   _____

2. "A fence sets men together, not apart." _____

   _____

3. " . . . I can't read or write. When a man cannot do those things, people think his head is

   weak." _____

   _____

4. "As to the work, what matters is that we have the back to do it." _____

   _____

5. "Every man must face his own mission." _____

   _____

Name: _____   Date: _____

A Day No Pigs Would Die—Chapters 9–15

Character Identification: Identify which character made each of the following statements in the book. Write the character's letter in the blank. You may use a character's letter more than once.

    (a) Haven Peck   (b) Robert   (c) Robert's mother   (d) Mr. Tanner

1. _____ "That's what being a man is all about. It's just doing what's got to be done."
2. _____ "There's no higher calling than animal husbandry, and making things live and grow."
3. _____ "I'm sure glad to be famed for something."
4. _____ "I'll buy your soap. Here, all I got is ten cents."
5. _____ "Pinky won a blue ribbon, Papa."
6. _____ "Rob worked my oxen like he was born with a wand in his hand."
7. _____ "He's back. Back from a dream."
8. _____ "Hussy, you got more spunk in you than a lot of us menfolk got brains."
9. _____ "So to short the story, I could be wrong. But I feel like it's over for me soon."
10. _____ "I'm glad we've got you to handle things. I couldn't of done it alone."

Essay: Answer the following questions in one or two complete paragraphs.

1. Describe the Shaker way of life as seen in the book.

2. As Robert grows to manhood what special memories do you think he will have of his father?

Name: _____   Date: _____

Final Test
A Day No Pigs Would Die

Multiple Choice: Choose the one best answer to each of the following questions. Write the letter of that choice in the blank.

1. _____ This book is set in rural   (a) Virginia   (b) California   (c) Vermont   (d) South Carolina.

2. _____ Robert's brothers are   (a) away at college   (b) married and living in a nearby county   (c) both dead   (d) in the army.

3. _____ Living with Robert and his family is   (a) Aunt Carrie   (b) Aunt Matty   (c) Uncle Tanner   (d) May.

4. _____ To pay Robert back for birthing his calf, Mr. Tanner gave Robert   (a) a kitten   (b) a pig   (c) five dollars   (d) a horse.

5. _____ Robert's father never voted because   (a) he hated politics   (b) it was too far to the polling places   (c) he was too busy with his work   (d) he couldn't read and write.

6. _____ Miss Sarah was   (a) Robert's teacher   (b) a cat   (c) Robert's aunt   (d) the milkcow.

7. _____ Aunt Matty said the problem with Robert's grammar was that he   (a) didn't know how to diagram   (b) didn't know the language well enough   (c) was too lazy   (d) didn't have a good teacher.

8. _____ After their first tutoring session, Aunt Matty said: (a) "Next time, I'll teach the pig."   (b) "You're the smartest child I've ever seen."   (c) "Ears and eyes closed—that's what you have."   (d) "You'll go far."

9. _____ Pinky was special to Robert because   (a) she was the first thing he ever owned   (b) he had earned her after working for a summer   (c) she was gift from his father   (d) she stayed in his room every night.

10. _____ When Robert's mother makes chocolate cake, he has to shoot a   (a) rabbit   (b) squirrel   (c) crow   (d) deer.

11. _____ Samson was   (a) Mr. Tanner's prize mule   (b) Mr. Tanner's boar   (c) the hired hand   (d) owner of Bob and Bib.

12. _____ Mr. Hillman went out in the middle of the night   (a) to save his herd   (b) to warn Robert's family of a flood   (c) to dig up a grave   (d) to set fire to the church.

13. _____ The gossip in the area is that Widow Bascom   (a) is drinking all the time   (b) is carrying on with the hired man   (c) is going to have a child   (d) just sits on her porch and stares.

14. _____ Robert goes to the Rutland Fair with   (a) Widow Bascom and Ira Long   (b) his Aunt Carrie   (c) his two best friends from school   (d) the Tanners.

15. _____ Pinky got a first-place ribbon for   (a) Best All-Round Pig   (b) Largest Pig   (c) Best Behaved Pig   (d) Best Color.

16. _____ After they weaseled the dog, Hussy, they had to   (a) shoot the weasel   (b) fix Hussy's leg   (c) take Hussy to the riverbank   (d) shoot Hussy.

Answer Key

A Day No Pigs Would Die (*Worksheet, Chapters 1–8*)

Character Identification

1. a
2. c
3. d
4. c
5. a

6. c
7. a
8. a
9. b
10. d

Comprehension (Answers may vary.)

1. If something feels as though its life is threatened, it will fight back, be it human or animal.

2. Fences are necessary between neighbors just to set up limits. These limits help everyone be better friends and neighbors.

3. Many people assume that an illiterate person is a stupid person. They judge the person on that one quality instead of looking beyond.

4. We should thank God that we are healthy enough to do the work put before us.

5. Every person's work is important in God's eyes and each person must be ready and willing to do the work that is needed, no matter how simple or menial.

A Day No Pigs Would Die (*Worksheet, Chapters 9–15*)

Character Identification

1. a
2. d
3. a
4. b
5. b

6. d
7. c
8. b
9. a
10. c

Essay (Answers will vary.)

1. The Shaker family seen in this book didn't believe in any "frills," and especially nothing extravagant on the Sabbath. All their clothes were hand-stitched by Rob's mother, and Rob's father never missed a day of work. The Shaker religion believed that each person had a mission and that work and the quality of that work was sacred. The Shakers worked honestly and owed nothing to anyone.

2. Robert will probably remember the quiet wisdom his father gave: how to be a good neighbor, the ethics of work, the duties of being a man, the importance of respecting people and animals. Robert will always remember the slaughter of Pinky, but at the same time, remember his father's empathy for him at this time.

Final Test

Multiple Choice

1. c	3. a	5. d	7. a	9. a	11. b	13. b	15. c
2. c	4. b	6. b	8. a	10. b	12. c	14. d	16. d

Extension Activities

A Day No Pigs Would Die

Discussion

CHAPTER 1

1. Instead of delivering the calf himself, what could Robert have done?
2. What were the advantages and disadvantages of delivering the calf right then?

CHAPTER 2

1. What does Robert's father do for a living?
2. What does the bedside conversation tell us about Robert's father?

CHAPTER 3

1. How did Shakers live?
2. What "common-sense" facts did Robert learn about cows and pigs?

CHAPTER 4

1. Which side would you agree with? Is Robert's family rich or poor?
2. What makes Robert feel like the luckiest boy in town?

CHAPTER 5

1. Describe Pinky's personality.
2. What does Robert regret about being a Shaker?

CHAPTER 6

1. Do you think the tutoring session helped Rob? Why or why not?

CHAPTER 7

1. How is living in rural Vermont in the 1920's different from living today?

CHAPTER 8

1. What had happened to Mr. Hillman?

CHAPTER 9

1. How does Robert's mother's opinion of Widow Bascom differ from Aunt Carrie's?
2. Why does Robert say that Widow Bascom is "much improved"?

CHAPTER 10

1. What did Haven Peck mean when he said, "Never miss a chance to keep your mouth shut"?
2. What happened at the fair?

CHAPTER 11

1. What happens when you "weasel a dog"?
2. What did Rob and the men feel like after the weaseling?

CHAPTER 12

1. What is Haven Peck known for in the county?
2. What does his father tell Rob in confidence?

CHAPTER 13

1. What did Rob decide about other religions?

CHAPTER 14

1. Why did Pinky have to die?
2. Why did Rob's father want Rob to be there during the butchering?

CHAPTER 15

1. What were Rob's responsibilities when his father died?

(continued)

A Day No Pigs Would Die (continued)

Reading

1. Robert Newton Peck has written many other books for young people. His whole *Soup* series is a popular choice for young readers. Here is a listing of some of his books.

Soup	*Soup in the Saddle*	*Trig Sees Red*	*Dukes*
Soup & Me	*Soup's Goat*	*Trig or Treat*	*Spanish Hoof*
Soup for President	*Soup on Ice*	*Clunie*	*Jo Silver*
Soup on Wheels	*Trig*		

2. Another excellent book that tells of a young boy's coming of age in rural America is *Where the Red Fern Grows* by Wilson Rawls. Set in the Oklahoma Ozarks during the 1930's, it also tells of a young boy's love for a pet. (This book is covered in Volume II of this series.)

Writing

1. Robert was very close to his father in this book. Have students choose a family member that they are close to and write a descriptive essay about that person. Included should be physical characteristics, mannerisms, and examples of caring. An additional project might include making these essays into pamphlets with covers and decorations and presenting them to the family member chosen as the subject of the essay.

2. The chapter about the Hillmans is a short but powerful one. Have students write another chapter that would tell what happened the next day between Mr. Hillman and his wife. Keep the language in first person (Robert's) and write as though he is witnessing what happens.

3. If a state fair is near to your community and students have frequently visited the fair, have them write about their very first time going to the fair.

Research

1. Most libraries will have a book or two on the Shakers. Have pairs of students research answers to the following questions:

   - How did the Shakers get their name?
   - What inventions have been credited to the Shakers?
   - What is their background or origin?
   - How did their religion differ from others?
   - Why has the religion almost died out?
   - Where were their settlements?

(continued)

- What is Shaker furniture?
- Who was Mother Ann Lee?
- How does Robert's family differ from the Shaker families found in your research?

2. A good book for young people to research and report on is *Shaker Inventions* by Sallie G. Randolph and Nancy O'Keefe Bolick.

3. Abner Doubleday is credited with creating the game of baseball. Have a student (or pair of students) research the beginnings of the game and Doubleday's contribution.

Drama

Several scenes from the book would be good for students to rewrite as plays. Have the students act out the following:

- Robert's tutoring session
- the Hillman scene
- the "fences" talk between Robert and his father
- Robert's visit to the fair

Are You There, God? It's Me, Margaret

by Judy Blume

Synopsis

Who can you believe, what exactly is normal, where do I fit in, and what do I believe . . . are all questions with answers that begin to take shape during Margaret's sixth-grade year. Margaret adapts to a new place, a new school, new friends, and discovers new questions about her life as she passes from eleven-something to twelve. In this mostly for girls young adult novel, Margaret weathers this often confusing year with candor and intelligence.

Vocabulary and Cultural Terminology

CHAPTER 1
1. inconvenient
2. commute
3. influence

CHAPTER 2
1. organdy
2. embraced

CHAPTER 3
1. demonstrated
2. limbs

CHAPTER 4
NONE

CHAPTER 5
1. reputation
2. sensation
3. situation
4. eloped

CHAPTER 6
1. confidential
2. cultural
3. lingerie

CHAPTER 7
1. eavesdropping

CHAPTER 8
1. parfait
2. rabbi
3. Rosh Hashanah
4. temple

CHAPTER 9
1. yarmulke
2. Hebrew
3. recite
4. Yom Tov

CHAPTER 10
1. incident
2. minister
3. devoted
4. chaperones

CHAPTER 11
1. prude

CHAPTER 12
1. custom
2. traditional
3. Hanukkah
4. Christmas
5. pageant

CHAPTER 13
1. sterile

CHAPTER 14
1. abominable

CHAPTER 15
1. menstruation
2. prompted

CHAPTER 16
1. subscription

CHAPTER 17
NONE

CHAPTER 18
1. committees

CHAPTER 19
1. confession
2. priest

CHAPTER 20
NONE

CHAPTER 21
1. entertaining
2. baptized

CHAPTERS 22 & 23
NONE

CHAPTER 24
1. conclusions
2. Judaism
3. Christianity
4. Catholicism

CHAPTER 25
NONE

Name: _____   Date: _____

Are You There, God? It's Me, Margaret—Chapters 1–12

Vocabulary: Fill in the blanks with appropriate words taken from the list below.

Hanukkah	Yom Tov	organdy	parfait
chaperones	lingerie	eloped	prude
confidential	eavesdropping	demonstrated	traditional

1. Nancy's brother and Moose were _____ outside the door as the girls did their bust exercises.

2. The man at the hardware store _____ the proper way for Margaret's father to run the lawn mower.

3. Mr. Benedict said it would be kept _____ if Margaret would explain why she doesn't like religious holidays.

4. Janie Loomis and her mother were shopping in the _____ department for the same reason Margaret was there with her mom.

5. Nancy's room had a dressing table, wrapped with _____ , that Margaret admired.

6. Nancy called Janie a _____ because Janie didn't think people should walk around naked.

7. Margaret's mom sends out cards at Christmas because it's a _____ American custom.

8. Some students refused to sing the Christmas and _____ songs during the pageant.

9. The _____ at the dance were dressed funny, like farmers or something.

10. The rabbi shook Margaret's hand and wished her good _____ .

11. Before the concert at Lincoln Center, Grandma bought Margaret a chocolate _____ at a restaurant.

12. Because their grandparents wouldn't accept a Jewish son-in-law, Margaret's parents _____ .

Character Identification: Write the name of the character next to his or her description.

Nancy	Father	Margaret	Grandma Sylvia

1. _____ Thought public transportation was dirty.

2. _____ Almost cut off a hand in the lawn mower.

3. _____ Said boys are disgusting because they are only interested in pictures of naked girls and dirty books.

4. _____ Hates religious holidays.

Are You There, God? It's Me, Margaret—Chapters 13–25

Vocabulary: Fill in the blanks with appropriate words taken from the list below.

priest	entertaining	conclusions	baptized	confession
sterile	menstruation	abominable	committees	subscription

1. Grandmother Hutchins thought Margaret should be a Christian because her mother had been _____ .

2. Mother knew about the movie at school explaining _____ .

3. In her letter to Mr. Benedict, Margaret said she had not reached any _____ about religion.

4. Mr. Benedict had already selected the students for the _____ because he wanted them to work with people they didn't know.

5. Margaret followed Laura to _____ but couldn't think of what to say.

6. Grandma had a _____ to the concerts at Lincoln Center.

7. Mrs. Fishbein said their behavior was _____ .

8. Mother made a special dinner for her parents; it was like she was _____ friends.

9. Margaret didn't understand that the confession booth was shared by a

   _____ .

10. Margaret knew her mother wouldn't mind her using the _____ cotton balls.

Short Essay: Using complete sentences, answer each of the following:

1. Contrast the image the girls have of Philip Leroy at the beginning of the book to the "real picture" Margaret has by the end of Chapter 18.

2. Describe Grandma Sylvia's relationship with Margaret.

3. Explain why Margaret is disappointed in her friend Nancy by the end of the book.

Name: _____   Date: _____

Final Test
Are You There, God? It's Me, Margaret

Character Identification: Write the character's letter in the blank next to each description of that character. You may use a letter more than once.

(a) Grandmother Hutchins   (e) Freddy   (i) Nancy

(b) Mr. Benedict   (f) Margaret   (j) Laura

(c) Moose   (g) Norman   (k) Grandma Sylvia

(d) Mother   (h) Philip

1. _____ Mother says she has too much influence on Margaret.

2. _____ Says not to believe things about people unless you see it yourself.

3. _____ Asked the class to please be prepared for the test.

4. _____ Counted hats in the synagogue and at church.

5. _____ Paints fruit pictures.

6. _____ Invited the whole class to a supper party.

7. _____ Blew mustard on the ceiling.

8. _____ Bought subscription tickets to Lincoln Center.

9. _____ Lied about getting her period.

10. _____ Told Margaret not to copy from the encyclopedia.

11. _____ Hasn't seen her daughter in fourteen years.

12. _____ Dates Mr. Binamin.

13. _____ Read three books about religion for the year-long project.

14. _____ Was eavesdropping with Evan during the Four PT's exercise meeting.

15. _____ Pinched Margaret on her birthday.

Short Essay: Answer the following questions in complete sentences.

1. In what ways did Margaret feel different from her friends?

2. Why was religion an important issue to Margaret?

Answer Key

Are You There, God? It's Me, Margaret (*Worksheet, Chapters 1–12*)

Vocabulary

1. eavesdropping
2. demonstrated
3. confidential
4. lingerie
5. organdy
6. prude
7. traditional
8. Hanukkah
9. chaperones
10. Yom Tov
11. parfait
12. eloped

Character Identification

1. Grandma Sylvia
2. Father
3. Nancy
4. Margaret

Are You There, God? It's Me, Margaret (*Worksheet, Chapters 13–25*)

Vocabulary

1. baptized
2. menstruation
3. conclusions
4. committee
5. confession
6. subscription
7. abominable
8. entertaining
9. priest
10. sterile

Short Essay (Answers will vary.)

1. The girls think he is very good-looking and they want to be with him as much as possible. At the beginning of the book, the girls all list him at the top of their "Boy Books." But as Margaret spends more time with him, she learns he is very immature and rude.

2. They are very close and involved in each other's lives. Grandma knits Margaret sweaters and calls and writes her. She arranges concert outings and vacations they can do together. They are honest and open with each other. Grandma Sylvia loves Margaret and hopes she becomes Jewish.

3. Margaret discovered that Nancy lied about getting her period and about Laura Danker's reputation.

Final Test

Character Identification

1. k
2. c
3. b
4. f
5. d
6. g
7. h
8. k
9. i
10. j
11. a
12. k
13. f
14. c
15. h

Short Essay (Answers will vary.)

1. Margaret didn't belong to a certain religion, she didn't have her period yet, and she wasn't developed.

2. Margaret wanted to belong, to have structure, and she was trying to understand her own faith in God.

Extension Activities

Are You There, God? It's Me, Margaret

Discussion

CHAPTER 1

1. Why was Margaret surprised about the move?

2. What does Margaret suspect is the real reason for the move?

CHAPTER 2

1. How is Margaret's mother different from the other neighborhood mothers?

2. In what ways does Margaret feel immature?

3. Describe Nancy.

4. How would you describe Margaret's relationship with God?

CHAPTER 3

1. List some of Grandma Sylvia's characteristics.

CHAPTER 4

1. Why is Mom concerned about Margaret having a first-year teacher?

CHAPTER 5

1. Describe Laura Danker.

2. Is there a difference between having a religion and being religious?

CHAPTER 6

1. Give examples of how Margaret is trying to "fit in."

CHAPTER 7

1. Is Mr. Benedict a good teacher? What makes you think so?

2. How did Mr. Benedict know who wrote each test paper?

CHAPTER 8

1. Is Margaret's mom overly concerned about her riding the bus alone? Explain.

CHAPTER 9

1. Why was Margaret disappointed after the service?

CHAPTER 10

1. Why would the PTA arrange a square dance for the students instead of a regular dance?

CHAPTER 11

1. What do you think is the reason or philosophy people have for going to a nudist colony?

CHAPTER 12

1. List examples in which religion has been a divisive factor so far in the book.

CHAPTERS 13 & 14

1. How does Philip Leroy behave at the party?

2. Do you think Laura Danker enjoyed the party? Why?

CHAPTER 15

1. In what ways does Margaret feel she isn't normal?

CHAPTERS 16 & 17

1. Do you think Grandma Sylvia should remarry? Why?

(continued)

2. How did Margaret's opinion of Nancy change in Chapter 17?

CHAPTER 18

1. Do you think Laura thinks of herself as normal? Why?

2. Why does Margaret feel that Nancy and Philip deserve each other?

CHAPTER 19

1. How do you think the story about Laura got started?

CHAPTER 20

1. Do you think Margaret was right to get so upset with her mother? Explain.

2. What do you think Margaret's mother hopes will happen when her parents visit?

CHAPTERS 21–23

1. Do you think religion is important to Margaret? Explain.

2. Grandma Sylvia said she came to support Margaret. What did she mean?

CHAPTERS 24 & 25

1. Did Margaret do much work on her project? Was it meaningful to her?

2. Why do you think Margaret begins to talk to God again in Chapter 25?

Reading

1. Judy Blume has written many popular books for young adults and children. Students who enjoyed this book may enjoy reading these novels by the same author:

Superfudge	*Then Again, Maybe I Won't*
Blubber	*Otherwise Known as Sheila the Great*
Freckle Juice	*Tales of a Fourth Grade Nothing*
*Deenie	*Sally J. Freedman as Herself*
Iggie's House	*Just As Long As We're Together*
It's Not the End of the World	*The Pain & the Great One*

*covered in Volume II of this series

2. Judy Blume has also written a nonfiction book entitled *Letters to Judy: What Kids Wish They Could Tell You*. For students who are interested in finding out more about Judy Blume this is a good place to start.

Writing

1. **Rewrite**—Rewrite Chapter 21. Pretend that Margaret's mother hires you to rewrite the chapter the way she hoped it would turn out.

2. **Sequel**—Imagine that Margaret happens to meet Mr. Benedict ten years later and tells him which religion she finally chose and why.

3. **Letters**—If Margaret could somehow have written a letter to her Grandmother Hutchins on the night her parents eloped, what advice would she have given?

(continued)

Research

1. Have class committees or individuals research information on the various religious holidays in the Christian and Jewish faiths.

2. The Catholic, Protestant, and Jewish religions all have ceremonies which mark attainment of the coming of age for girls within the faith. Have committees or individuals research the Jewish Bat Mitzvah, the Catholic Quinceanera (related to Mexican culture), and the Protestant Confirmation.

Drama

Rewrite in play form and act out Chapter 21.

No Place for Me

by Barthe DeClements

Synopsis

It truly seems that there is no place for 12-year-old Copper. Her mother is in an alcohol rehabilitation center and her stepfather wants out of the marriage. After disastrous results from staying with two different sets of relatives, Copper ends up with her Aunt Maggie, who is rumored to be a "real witch." After much suspicion and distrust, Copper learns to believe in herself and, with the help of her aunt, take control of her own fears.

Vocabulary

CHAPTER 1
1. davenport

CHAPTER 2
1. rummaging
2. indignant
3. manipulate

CHAPTER 3
NONE

CHAPTER 4
1. shears
2. wedge
3. squalling
4. mimicking
5. cringe

CHAPTER 5
1. distract
2. dismissal

CHAPTER 6
1. amber
2. stern
3. dense

CHAPTER 7
1. suspicious
2. prattled
3. sauntered

CHAPTER 8
1. wavering
2. self-righteousness
3. exasperation
4. prig
5. flatter

CHAPTER 9
1. canopy

CHAPTER 10
1. rigid
2. premises
3. commitment

CHAPTER 11
1. stability
2. incumbent
3. prejudiced
4. frantically
5. disastrous
6. bitterly

CHAPTER 12
1. visualization
2. antidote
3. acquire
4. hex
5. corridor
6. linear
7. perception
8. botany

CHAPTER 13
1. clammy

CHAPTER 14
1. cloak
2. entangled

CHAPTER 15
1. specimens
2. cult
3. tarot cards
4. maneuver

CHAPTER 16
1. trowel
2. clairvoyants
3. belfry
4. spire
5. tactful

CHAPTER 17
1. coven

CHAPTER 18
1. stranded
2. lavatory
3. resourceful

Name: _____ Date: _____

No Place for Me—Chapters 1–9

Multiple Response: Choose as many responses as are needed in order to complete the statement or question correctly. This means you may write as many as all four letters in the blank, or just one.

1. _____ Copper was upset at the beginning of the book because (a) her mother was in a rehab center (b) her cousins were coming to stay with them (c) her stepfather was moving away (d) she would have to go live with someone else.

2. _____ When Copper was staying at her Aunt Dorothy's she was upset by (a) having to share a room with Sarah (b) having a dirty quilt on her bed (c) having to do the supper dishes (d) Brenda's attitude toward her.

3. _____ Aunt Dorothy showed favoritism toward her own girls by (a) not speaking to Copper (b) not buying Copper any clothes or ice cream (c) telling her daughters not to let Copper "manipulate" them (d) making her do more chores.

4. _____ Copper got into trouble at Aunt Dorothy's when (a) she left the bike out in the rain (b) she forgot about Sarah after school (c) she lied and went to a skating rink instead of the movie (d) she took some money out of her aunt's purse.

5. _____ Being sent to Uncle Raymond's was a different experience because (a) they had no children (b) Copper had the most beautiful room all to herself (c) they left for weeks at a time and left Copper by herself (d) they were so poor.

Vocabulary: Use words from the vocabulary lists for Chapters 1–9 in order to fill in the blanks correctly.

1. Copper sat on the _____ and listened to Jeff's news about moving.

2. She picked up the _____ and began cutting her daughter's hair.

3. Copper's eyes were dark _____ .

4. Copper gave Brenda a small, _____ smile, but it didn't help much.

5. Aunt Dorothy's _____ was beginning to show on her tight, worried face.

6. The bed had a _____ which delighted Copper.

7. Copper tried to _____ her mom from talking about the rehab center.

8. Copper heard Brenda _____ her voice, saying "My hair's my best feature."

9. They _____ on about the movie even though Aunt Dorothy and Uncle Tom were looking more suspicious.

10. Sarah was _____ that Copper would accuse her of bed-wetting.

Short Essay: Write a well-developed paragraph to answer the following question.

At this point in the book, what do you think is Copper's biggest problem?

Name: _____   Date: _____

No Place for Me—Chapters 10–18

Comprehension: Fill in the blanks with words, phrases, and even names from the book that would make sense in the context of the story.

1. At Aunt Judith's, Copper was involved in a _____ .

2. At Aunt Maggie's there was a _____ instead of a conventional bed.

3. For an earache, Aunt Maggie used _____ .

4. To help Copper feel safe at night her aunt got her a _____ .

5. Copper and _____ hid in the woods so they could watch the

   _____ .

6. Aunt Maggie told Copper to _____ of her dreams.

7. Aunt Maggie agreed to take Copper to the _____ to see the boy Copper liked

   named _____ .

8. In the end, Copper decides to live with _____ .

Matching: Match up the definitions of witchcraft-related terms. Write the letter of the definition in the blank next to the correct word.

1. _____ scrying   (a) Study of plants

2. _____ hex   (b) A group of witches

3. _____ botany   (c) A curse

4. _____ cult   (d) A doll made to resemble a real person

5. _____ tarot cards   (e) A term used in meetings that means "So must it be"

6. _____ clairvoyants   (f) A group of people dedicated to one cause

7. _____ coven   (g) Remote viewing

8. _____ poppet   (h) Method used to help concentrate on a problem

9. _____ So mote it be.   (i) A natural antibiotic

10. _____ garlic   (j) People who can see what others are doing

Short Essay: Write a well-developed paragraph to answer the following question.

What misconceptions did Copper have about "witches"?

Name: _____ Date: _____

Final Test
No Place for Me

Character Identification: Write the character's letter in the blank next to each description of that character. You may use a letter more than once.

(a) Copper   (c) Aunt Judith   (e) Denise

(b) Aunt Dorothy   (d) Aunt Maggie   (f) Copper's mom

1. _____ Shuffled from one relative to another.
2. _____ Gave preferential treatment to own girls.
3. _____ Was a "white witch."
4. _____ Called Anath by some people.
5. _____ Very interested in her husband's political career.
6. _____ Had to hide in a bathroom stall.
7. _____ Was definitely not a good hair cutter.
8. _____ Thought she and Jeff could still patch things up.
9. _____ Her only brother was Copper's father.
10. _____ Gave Copper a room with a beautiful canopy bed.
11. _____ She and her husband had to leave Copper for just one evening.
12. _____ Spied with Copper on the witches' meeting.
13. _____ Took Copper to the skating rink and read while Copper skated.
14. _____ Refused to change the quilt on Copper's bed.
15. _____ Student who lived near Copper's Aunt Maggie.

Short Essay: Write at least one well-developed paragraph to answer each of the following questions.

1. How did Copper change and mature throughout the book?

2. How is Aunt Maggie a better aunt to Copper than the other two were?

Answer Key

No Place For Me *(Worksheet, Chapters 1–9)*

Multiple Response

1. a, c, d	4. b, c
2. a, b	5. a, b
3. b, c	

Vocabulary

1. davenport	5. exasperation	8. mimicking
2. shears	6. canopy	9. prattled
3. amber	7. distract	10. indignant
4. wavering		

Short Essay (Answers will vary.)

Some answers might be: (a) not belonging anywhere, (b) feeling deserted by her mom/stepfather/others, (c) new schools/new friends—being accepted, (d) feelings of rejection.

No Place for Me *(Worksheet, Chapters 10–18)*

Comprehension

1. burglary	6. take control
2. futon	7. skating rink,
3. garlic	Ricky Layton
4. telephone	8. Aunt Maggie
5. Denise, witches	

Matching

1. g	4. f	7. b	9. e
2. c	5. h	8. d	10. i
3. a	6. j		

Short Essay (Answers will vary.)

Some answers might be: (a) All witches put curses on people, (b) witches are evil, (c) witches can't have anything to do with religion, (d) witches are ugly, mean, and cruel.

Final Test

Character Identification

1. a	3. d	5. c	7. b	9. d	11. c	13. d	15. e
2. b	4. d	6. a	8. f	10. c	12. e	14. b	

Short Essay (Answers will vary.)

1. Some answers might be: (a) Copper no longer tries to get her own way all the time, (b) Copper is more honest with her aunt, (c) she has taken control of her fears, (d) she is more realistic about her future.

2. Some answers might be: (a) she really listens to Copper; tries to understand, (b) treats Copper like an adult; respects her feelings, (c) helps her with her problems.

Extension Activities

No Place for Me

Discussion

CHAPTER 1

1. Why has Copper always been scared of Aunt Maggie?

2. Where is Jeff going? Why?

3. Why did the room arrangements at Aunt Dorothy's upset Copper?

CHAPTER 2

1. What argument do Copper and Sarah have on Copper's first night there?

2. How did Copper take care of the quilt? Was there a better way to handle this problem?

CHAPTER 3

1. How does Aunt Dorothy show preference for her own girls and exclude Copper?

2. What kind of person is Aunt Dorothy?

CHAPTER 4

1. How does Copper intend to get the money to have her hair cut?

2. Is Copper really a manipulating person? Explain.

CHAPTER 5

1. How does Copper meet Ricky Layton?

2. How is Copper a little disappointed in her new school?

CHAPTER 6

1. How did Copper get into trouble concerning Brenda?

CHAPTER 7

1. Why does Copper think of Sarah as "a big baby"?

2. What plot do Copper and Kim come up with? Why doesn't it work out the way they planned?

CHAPTER 8

1. Why was Copper ousted from Aunt Dorothy's house?

2. How did Copper's mother console her through this move?

CHAPTER 9

1. How was Aunt Judith's house a different kind of experience for Copper?

2. How was her first day at her new school a disaster?

CHAPTER 10

1. Did Copper think reasonably during the burglary? Is there anything else she could have done?

CHAPTER 11

1. Why did Copper's Uncle Raymond feel that Copper couldn't stay with them?

2. What present did Aunt Judith give to Copper? Why? Why didn't Copper thank her for the present?

CHAPTER 12

1. How is Aunt Maggie's life-style different from that of the other aunts?

2. How did Aunt Maggie make Copper's first day at her new school easier on her?

CHAPTER 13

1. Why do you think Copper is having nightmares?

(continued)

2. What does Aunt Maggie say about being a witch? What are her powers?

CHAPTER 14

1. Why do you think that Copper's mom is frightened of the future?

2. How is Aunt Maggie a better aunt to Copper than her other two?

CHAPTER 15

1. Why was the phone a perfect gift for Copper?

2. How does Aunt Maggie explain the use of tarot cards?

CHAPTER 16

1. What compromise does Aunt Maggie make with Copper about her fancy dinner on Friday night?

CHAPTER 17

1. How is Denise and Copper's plan deceitful?

CHAPTER 18

1. How did Copper "change" her dream?

2. Why do you think Copper agreed to keep living with Aunt Maggie?

Reading

1. Barthe DeClements has written other books for young people. Appropriate for middle-school-age students are the following:

   How Do You Lose Those Ninth Grade Blues?
   Nothing's Fair in the Fifth Grade
   Sixth Grade Can Really Kill You
   Double Trouble (written with Christopher Greimes)

2. Witchcraft can be an interesting research project for young people. Any books or sections in encyclopedias about the Salem Witch Trials would reveal facts about this unfair time in American history. The fictional account *The Witch of Blackbird Pond* by Elizabeth George Speare was a Newberry Award winner and still draws readers today.

3. Many books for young adults deal with displaced young people and their special problems. The following books all deal with young people living in new and strange surroundings, with their particular themes.

   * *The Pinballs* by Betsy Byars (foster homes)
   Home Before Dark by Sue Ellen Bridges (migrant workers; parental death)
   Kentucky Daughter by Carol J. Scott (move from rural to city school)
   Homesick—My Own Story by Jean Fritz (move from China to U.S.—nonfiction)
   The Broccoli Tapes by Jan Slepian (move to Hawaii)
   The Atami Dragons by David Klass (move to Japan; parental death)
   The Orphan Train Quartet books by Joan Lowery Nixon (foster children)

   * covered in this volume

Drama

Many of the chapters of this book contain lots of conversation. Have students rewrite and edit a chapter into play form and then act it out.

The Sign of the Beaver
by Elizabeth George Speare

Synopsis

In the spring of 1768, Matt and his father homestead land in the Maine territory. In early summer Father leaves Matt alone to protect the cabin and fields while he returns to Massachusetts for Matt's mother, sister, and the new baby. Father predicts the journey will take six to seven weeks, but when winter comes they still haven't returned. Matt survives, thanks to the lessons he learns from his Indian neighbors; and Matt's coming of age parallels that of his Indian friend.

Vocabulary

CHAPTER 1
1. surveyor
2. notch
3. reassure

CHAPTER 2
1. venturing
2. proprietors
3. solitary
4. deacon

CHAPTER 3
1. deliberately

CHAPTER 4
1. salvage

CHAPTER 5
1. endure
2. persuaded
3. glimpse

CHAPTER 6
1. leggings
2. occur
3. breechcloth
4. despise
5. scorn
6. incomprehensible
7. defiance

CHAPTER 7
1. heathen
2. disdainfully
3. rigid

CHAPTER 8
NONE

CHAPTER 9
1. snare
2. nonchalantly
3. devised
4. contemptuous
5. cannibal

CHAPTER 10
NONE

CHAPTER 11
1. disposition

CHAPTER 12
1. envious
2. stalking
3. earnestly
4. chagrined
5. yielded

CHAPTER 13
1. indignant
2. shrewdly

CHAPTER 14
NONE

CHAPTER 15
1. solemnness
2. tribute

CHAPTER 16
1. nimbly
2. entranced
3. stockade
4. pungent
5. medley
6. boisterous

CHAPTER 17
1. genial

CHAPTER 18
1. summon
2. substantial
3. relenting
4. adoration

CHAPTER 19
1. forfeit
2. ordeal

CHAPTER 20
NONE

CHAPTER 21
1. unhampered
2. comradeship

CHAPTER 22
NONE

CHAPTER 23
1. ventured
2. intricately

CHAPTER 24
NONE

CHAPTER 25
1. typhus
2. clamor

Name: _____   Date: _____

The Sign of the Beaver—Chapters 1-12

Vocabulary: Using the vocabulary words listed below, fill in the blanks with appropriate choices.

rigid	deliberately	heathen
reassure	deacons	stalking
yielded	nonchalantly	despise
cannibal	salvage	endure
envious	surveyor	disposition

1. Matt felt the need to _____ his father before he left, but he was tongue-tied.

2. Matt was swinging the rabbit _____ as he had seen Attean do.

3. Matt doubted those porcupine quills had improved his dog's looks or his _____ .

4. It seemed impossible that the bow wood would bend, but slowly it _____ and the string slipped over the notch.

5. Attean sat down as straight and _____ as a cedar post.

6. Matt felt he could scarcely _____ another meal of plain fish.

7. Ben stood still, _____ taking his time looking over the cornfield and the cabin.

8. Father spread out the _____ 's map and traced the boundaries of the land he purchased in Maine territory.

9. Matt thought it would be silly to explain religious alphabet rhymes to this _____ boy.

10. Matt and his old friends used to play like "Indians," _____ each other through the woods.

11. Matt was _____ of the bow Attean carried behind his shoulder.

12. Crusoe's man, Friday, narrowly escaped being part of the _____ feast.

13. Attean stared around the cabin and seemed to _____ everything he saw.

14. The best Matt could do was _____ two handfuls of gritty meal off the dirt floor.

15. The two men nodded to each other gravely, as if they had been two church _____ .

Trivia Busters: Fill in the blanks with a word or phrase taken from the context of the book.

1. Aremus means _____ in Attean's language.

2. Piz Wat means _____ in Attean's language.

Name: _____ Date: _____

The Sign of the Beaver—Chapters 13–25

Vocabulary: Using the vocabulary words listed below, fill in the blanks with appropriate choices.

shrewdly	genial	pungent	substantial
stockade	typhus	ventured	entranced
indignant	intricately		

1. The Indian village was surrounded by a _____ of upright wooden posts.

2. When the winter weather set in, Matt rarely _____ outside without his snowshoes.

3. His family had been delayed due to an outbreak of _____ .

4. Attean's grandmother lived in the most _____ cabin in the village.

5. During the celebration Attean was in a friendly, _____ mood.

6. The fragrance of boiling meat and _____ herbs made Matt hungry.

7. Grandfather had _____ paired the two boys who could learn so much from each other.

8. Attean was _____ to think that Matt would even consider hunting in another clan's territory.

9. Matt was _____ by the silent speed as Attean paddled on the silver river.

10. Attean showed Matt how to construct a trap built of heavy logs _____ balanced above the bait.

Trivia Busters: Answer the following questions in one or two sentences.

1. How did Matt finally gain Attean's respect?

2. How will the manitou come to Attean?

3. What did Attean whisper to the bear?

4. Why isn't Marie called by an Indian name?

5. Matt's and Attean's cultures tell what similar story?

Name: _____   Date: _____

Final Test
The Sign of the Beaver

Sequencing: Number from 1 to 10 in the correct order in which these events happened in the book.

_____ Saknis rescues Matt from the bees.

_____ The boys kill the bear.

_____ Matt and Father build the cabin.

_____ Matt and Marie rescue the dog.

_____ Ben steals the gun.

_____ Matt tries to teach Attean the alphabet.

_____ Attean gives Matt the dog.

_____ Father gives Matt the watch.

_____ Attean finds his manitou.

_____ Saknis and Attean ask Matt to live with them.

Character Identification: In the blank, write the name of the character who is identified by the phrase or sentence. You may use a name more than once.

Ben	Attean	Matt	Mother
Father	Saknis	Marie	Aremus

1. _____ Had porcupine needles in the nose.

2. _____ Was the leader of the Indian clan.

3. _____ Told stories from the book to Indian brothers every night.

4. _____ Gave a book to the old Indian.

5. _____ Was baptized by the French Jesuit father.

6. _____ Had the worst case of typhus.

7. _____ Said he had been taken captive by the Iroquois.

8. _____ Threw a rabbit at the bear.

9. _____ Said it would be better to die than be a slave.

10. _____ Was caught in a trap.

11. _____ His hair had been newly shaved except for the topknot.

12. _____ Gave the Indian boy a watch.

13. _____ His mother was killed for her scalp.

14. _____ She was excited about the new neighbors that would settle.

15. _____ Grandfather gave him a new rifle.

Answer Key

The Sign of the Beaver *(Worksheet, Chapters 1–12)*

Vocabulary

1. reassure	4. yielded	7. deliberately	10. stalking	13. despise
2. nonchalantly	5. rigid	8. surveyor	11. envious	14. salvage
3. disposition	6. endure	9. heathen	12. cannibal	15. deacons

Trivia Busters

1. dog
2. "good for nothing"

The Sign of the Beaver *(Worksheet, Chapters 13–25)*

Vocabulary

1. stockade	3. typhus	5. genial	7. shrewdly	9. entranced
2. ventured	4. substantial	6. pungent	8. indignant	10. intricately

Trivia Busters

1. He gained his respect by staying at the cabin to wait for his family.

2. He must go out into the forest alone and take special medicine: it will come in a dream.

3. He asked its forgiveness that he had to kill.

4. She was baptized by a priest.

5. They tell about a flood and about sending out a bird to see if the water had receded.

Final Test

Sequencing

4, 6, 1, 7, 3, 5, 10, 2, 8, 9

Character Identification

1. Aremus	5. Marie	9. Attean	13. Attean
2. Saknis	6. Mother	10. Aremus	14. Mother
3. Attean	7. Ben	11. Attean	15. Attean
4. Matt	8. Matt	12. Matt	

Extension Activities

The Sign of the Beaver

Discussion

CHAPTER 1

1. Why is Matt left behind at the cabin?
2. How does Father recommend that Matt keep track of time?
3. How long will Father be gone?

CHAPTER 2

1. What was Father's advice about Indians?
2. Why was the fire so important to Matt?

CHAPTER 3

1. How does Matt greet the stranger?
2. Why is Matt concerned about Ben staying with him?
3. What does the loss of the rifle mean to Matt?

CHAPTER 4

1. How did the bear get into the cabin?
2. What relationship do the little pumpkins have with the family's return?

CHAPTER 5

1. How does Matt escape the bees?
2. Why was the old Indian reaching for Matt's throat?

CHAPTER 6

1. Why does Matt give away the book?
2. Why does Saknis want his grandson to read?

CHAPTER 7

1. Why didn't Matt teach Attean the alphabet in the same way he learned himself?
2. Why did Attean leave the cabin?

CHAPTER 8

1. What did Matt mean when he said Crusoe lived like a king?
2. How has Matt gotten Attean interested in learning?

CHAPTER 9

1. In what new ways is Matt understanding the book?
2. How is Attean keeping his grandfather's treaty?

CHAPTER 10

1. What abilities do the boys respect in each other?
2. How does Matt "change" the book for Attean?

CHAPTER 11

1. How did Attean show that he trusted Matt?
2. What does Matt learn from Attean in this chapter?

CHAPTER 12

1. In what ways are the boys working together?
2. What is the "Indian way" to make a bow?

CHAPTER 13

1. How does Matt know Attean is learning?
2. Why don't the boys free the fox?

CHAPTER 14

1. How are the biblical and Indian stories of the flood similar?

(continued)

2. How do we know that Attean really enjoyed *Robinson Crusoe?*

CHAPTER 15

1. How does the rabbit help the boys?
2. Why does Attean apologize to the bear?

CHAPTER 16

1. Why did Matt feel a strong need to talk with his father?
2. Why doesn't Attean join the feasting?

CHAPTER 17

1. What "wall" separates the boys?
2. Why are the beaver scarce?

CHAPTER 18

1. How does Marie help Matt free the dog?
2. Why does Matt stay only in the territory of the beaver?

CHAPTER 19

1. What test does Matt pass?
2. Why was Matt so interested in squaw work?

CHAPTER 20

1. What test does Attean face?

2. How will the manitou change their friendship?

CHAPTER 21

1. How has Attean changed?
2. Why won't the Indians return?

CHAPTER 22

1. Why did Matt feel that Attean made sense about owning land?
2. Why did Matt give away the watch?

CHAPTER 23

1. How does Matt set about pleasing his absent family?
2. What Indian ways is Matt adopting?

CHAPTER 24

1. How do the snowshoes set Matt free?
2. Why does Matt have to have access to the forest?

CHAPTER 25

1. How has Matt changed?
2. How has his family changed?

Reading

1. Students who enjoyed this book may enjoy reading these books by the same author:

   Calico Captive
   The Witch of Blackbird Pond

2. Some other books about Native Americans that students may enjoy are:

   Streams to the River, River to the Sea by Scott O'Dell
   The Story of Sacajawea, Guide to Lewis and Clark by Della Rowland
   The Incredible Journey of Lewis and Clark by Roda Blumberg
   Brothers of the Heart by Joan Blos
   The Bone Wars by Kathryn Lasky
   Buffalo Hunt by Russell Freedman
   Quantah Parker by Len Helts

(continued)

Only Earth and Sky Last Forever by Nathaniel Benchley
* *Julie of the Wolves* by Jean Craighead George
Jenny of the Tetons by Kristiana Gregory
Sweetgrass by Jan Hudson
* *The Indian in the Cupboard* by Lynn Reid Banks

* covered in this volume

Writing

1. If Matt could have gotten one letter out to his parents around the end of September, what would he have told them? Have students work in small groups to construct a letter from Matt. Have the groups compare the information contained in their letters.

2. Have students write an epilogue for this book from Attean's perspective after ten years. Where would Attean's clan be? What would he foresee as the future for the tribe and Native Americans in general? How would he feel about his experiences with Matt?

3. Have students construct a characterization web for each of the boys in this book. What values do the boys share? What are their major differences?

Research

1. Have students research the Western Movement with a focus on the effects the movement had on Native Americans.

2. Have students research the history of the Five Civilized Tribes.

3. Have students research creation myths of various cultures.

4. Have students research the art of the Native American. How do the art forms differ from northern tribes to southern tribes? How are they alike?

Art

1. Have students illustrate a new book cover for the book.

2. Have students do some of the drawings they found for assignment 4 in the Research section above and give a presentation to the class.

FAMILY PROBLEMS/ SPECIAL RELATIONSHIPS

Bridge to Terabithia

by Katherine Paterson

Synopsis

Jess Aarons lives on a farm with his parents and four sisters. Leslie Burke and her parents move to the country to get away from materialism. Although Jess and Leslie have little in common, the creation of "Terabithia," their magical kingdom in the forest nearby, solidifies their friendship. Leslie brings magic to Jess's world, and when she accidentally dies in a drowning accident, he learns to take that magic with him for the rest of his life.

Vocabulary

CHAPTER 1
1. obedient
2. fetch
3. prim
4. discarded

CHAPTER 2
1. pandemonium
2. hypocritical
3. snare

CHAPTER 3
1. repulsive
2. declaration
3. conspicuous
4. drought
5. sarcasm

CHAPTER 4
1. consolation
2. ominous
3. contempt
4. intoxicated
5. foes

CHAPTER 5
1. stronghold
2. parapets
3. crimson

CHAPTER 6
1. obsessed
2. consolidated
3. speculation
4. surplus
5. grieve
6. grove

CHAPTER 7
1. exiled
2. dregs
3. tolerated
4. "mother lode"
5. realm
6. hostile
7. jester
8. vile

CHAPTER 8
1. wheedling
2. clambered
3. pew
4. unison
5. genuine

CHAPTER 9
1. beige
2. vanquished
3. repented
4. sporadically

CHAPTER 10
1. suppress
2. kinship
3. myth

CHAPTER 11
1. relentless
2. dredging

CHAPTER 12
1. cremated

CHAPTER 13
1. sacred
2. traitorous
3. allegiance
4. fragile
5. predators

Name: _____   Date: _____

Bridge to Terabithia—Chapters 1–6

Crossword Puzzle: Use vocabulary words and characters from the book to fill in the puzzle.

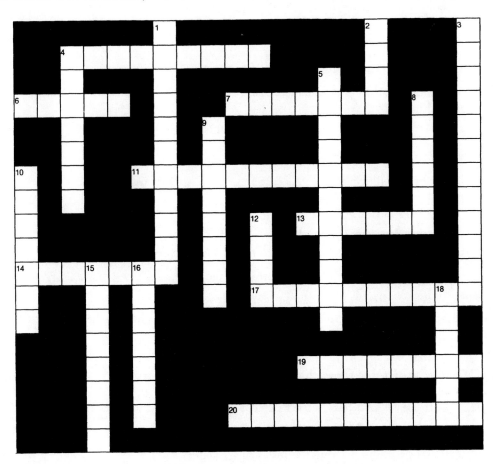

Across Clues

4. Jess _____ his T-shirt before the race.
6. The place would be in the _____ of trees.
7. An _____ look crossed Leslie's face as the teacher mentioned TV.
11. Jess tried not to be too _____ the first school day.
13. At first, Jess and Leslie wanted to get revenge on _____ .
14. Jess could hear the _____ in his voice.
17. Terabithia was their _____ .
19. Jess's younger sister.
20. Jess was _____ with Miss Edmunds' magical ways.

Down Clues

1. It was complete _____ at school the first day.
2. There were no _____ that Leslie and Jess could not defeat.
3. There was one _____ high school.
4. The ground had hardened from the summer _____ .
5. Jess's only _____ was that no one would beat Leslie.
8. Leslie didn't _____ much about having to leave her old school.
9. During the holidays, Jess's sisters were _____ with presents.
10. His face turned _____ when Leslie waved to him.
12. He was the only boy in a family of four girls.
15. They looked at Leslie with _____ when she said she didn't have a TV.
16. Jess's parents would never have a _____ to buy things.
18. She wrote a theme on scuba diving.

Name: _____   Date: _____

Bridge to Terabithia—Chapters 7-12

Vocabulary: Using the vocabulary list below, fill in the blanks with appropriate words.

fragile	kinship	realm	sporadically	vile
genuine	pew	sacred	traitorous	wheedling

1. Prince Terrien became the guardian of the _____ .

2. Leslie tried to find a word that was _____ enough to describe Janice's "friends," but couldn't.

3. Ellie used her _____ voice whenever she wanted her own way.

4. In church, they sat in the very first _____ .

5. Leslie's questions about religion were _____ , not just sarcastic ones.

6. The rain continued _____ all week long.

7. Jess felt a kind of _____ with the other artists.

8. Jess carried the _____ wreath to the grove of trees.

9. Jess began to realize that their world at Terabithia was a very _____ one that had to be nurtured.

10. Jess felt a little _____ toward Leslie when he thought how he would be the fastest runner now.

True/False: Write *true* or *false* for each of the following statements.

1. _____ Both Leslie and Jess helped Leslie's dad paint the living room gold.

2. _____ Leslie told Jess that her half-friend at school was now May Belle.

3. _____ P.T. was the nickname for Jess's older sister.

4. _____ At Christmas Leslie told Jess she wanted to go with him to church.

5. _____ Jess was really frightened of going across the river that had risen so high from the rains.

6. _____ When Leslie drowned, Jess was at an art museum with his father.

7. _____ Leslie drowned when the old rope broke over the water.

8. _____ Jess made Janice the new Princess of Terabithia.

9. _____ The day after Leslie's death Jess cried in the barn almost all day long.

10. _____ Bill thanked Jess for being such a wonderful friend to Leslie.

Name: _____   Date: _____

Final Test
Bridge to Terabithia

Character Identification: Match the quotation with the character who said it in the book. Write the character's letter in the blank. You may use a letter more than once.

(a) Jess   (b) Leslie   (c) May Belle   (d) Bill

1. _____ "Jess, you shouldn't ought to beat me in the head."
2. _____ "My parents are reassessing their value structure."
3. _____ "We need a whole secret country and you and I would be the rulers of it."
4. _____ "She stole my Twinkies!"
5. _____ "Jess. I know where you and Leslie go to hide."
6. _____ "Methinks some evil being has put a curse on our beloved kingdom."
7. _____ "Leslie wouldn't drown. She could swim real good."
8. _____ "Everybody gets scared sometimes, May Belle. You don't have to be ashamed."
9. _____ "I meant to give you P.T., but I can't seem to give him up."
10. _____ "There's a rumor going around that the beautiful girl arriving today might be the queen they've been waiting for."

Contrasting Details: In the spaces below write the differences between Leslie and Jess.

	JESS	LESLIE
1. LIFE-STYLE		
2. RELATIONSHIP WITH FATHER		
3. TALENTS		
4. FEARS		
5. TYPE OF PERSONALITY		
6. CREATIVITY		

Answer Key

Bridge to Terabithia (Crossword Puzzle, Chapters 1–6)

Crossword Puzzle

Word List (for optional use with students)

conspicuous	drought	Janice	pandemonium
consolidated	foes	Jess	sarcasm
consolation	grove	Leslie	stronghold
contempt	grieve	May Belle	
crimson	surplus	obsessed	
discarded	intoxicated	ominous	

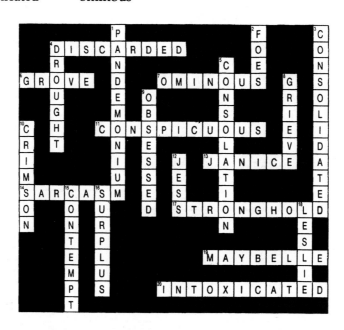

Bridge to Terabithia (Worksheet, Chapters 7–12)

Vocabulary

1. realm
2. vile
3. wheedling
4. pew
5. genuine
6. sporadically
7. kinship
8. sacred
9. fragile
10. traitorous

True/False

1. true
2. false
3. false
4. false
5. true
6. false
7. true
8. false
9. false
10. true

(continued)

Final Test

Character Identification

1. c	6. b
2. b	7. a
3. b	8. a
4. c	9. d
5. c	10. a

Contrasting Details

Students' answers may vary. These are some of the ideas that could apply.

JESS	LESLIE
1. Poor farming family; sisters are materialistic; noisy with five kids; money always a problem.	"Yuppies" who moved to the country: have discarded materialism (no TV); quiet life-style with classical music; money not a problem.
2. Wants more from father; until Leslie's death, almost no conversation.	Close, calls him "Bill"; helps him paint house; trusting.
3. Artistic talents.	Writes well; imaginative; understands people well; adventurous (scuba diving).
4. Crossing river; fearful of life in general.	Displays almost no fears.
5. Shy, reserved, needs someone like Leslie to draw him out; discontented with family.	Trusting, happy with life.
6. Creates artwork.	Creates idea of Terabithia; creates scheme to get Janice.

Extension Activities

Bridge to Terabithia

Discussion

CHAPTER 1
1. Describe Jess's home life.
2. What is Jess's one goal as the new school year approaches? How might this actually be attainable?

CHAPTER 2
1. What does Jess reveal about his relationship with his father?
2. Why did Jess like Miss Edmunds so much?

CHAPTER 3
1. Why was Jess jealous of Leslie?
2. How does Leslie break the "rules" of the playground?

CHAPTER 4
1. Why did the recess races end?
2. Jess says when he first smiled at Leslie that "it was the beginning of a new season in his life." What does this mean?
3. Describe Terabithia.

CHAPTER 5
1. How did Jess and Leslie "defeat" the real-life giant, Janice Avery?

CHAPTER 6
1. Who was Prince Terrien?
2. How was Jess's Christmas with his family less than what he wanted?

CHAPTER 7
1. Why was it "no good" for Jess to go to Terabithia alone?
2. Why do you think Leslie seemed happier than everyone else?

3. What revelation about Janice Avery did Jess and Leslie discover?

CHAPTER 8
1. Why do you think Leslie wanted to go to church?
2. What do Leslie and Jess argue about concerning God and religion?

CHAPTER 9
1. What is the "Evil Spell" that the chapter is talking about?
2. What fear does Jess try to conceal from Leslie? Why does he cover it up?

CHAPTER 10
1. What was Jess's "perfect day"? Why did it seem perfect to him?
2. Why will he feel guilty when he returns home?

CHAPTER 11
1. How does Jess react to Leslie's death immediately? the next morning?

CHAPTER 12
1. Why did Jess feel more alone than ever at the Burkes' house?
2. How did Jess's father console him at this time?

CHAPTER 13
1. What kind of final tribute did Jess give to Leslie?
2. Why do you think May Belle followed Jess into the woods?
3. What discovery does Jess make about Mrs. Myers, his teacher?
4. How does Jess carry on Leslie's magic?

(continued)

42

Reading

1. Katherine Paterson has written many beautiful books for young people. The following could be given to groups or individuals as a follow-up to *Bridge to Terabithia.* (**E = Easy, M = Medium, D = Difficult**)

   Come Sing, Jimmy Jo (M)   *Of Nightingales That Weep* (D)
   The Great Gilly Hopkins (E)   * *Park's Quest* (M)
   Jacob Have I Loved (D)   ** *Rebels of the Heavenly Kingdom* (D)
   The Master Puppeteer (D)   *The Sign of the Chrysanthemum* (D)

       * covered in this volume
    ** covered in Volume II of this series

2. Because the kingdom of Narnia from *The Chronicles of Narnia* by C. S. Lewis is alluded to so much in the book, assign the reading of *The Lion, the Witch and the Wardrobe* (the first book in the *Chronicles*).

3. *The Little Prince* by Antoine de Saint-Exupéry is a simple-to-read allegory which provides wonderful discussion ideas about friendship and death. Have the class read it together (or the teacher could read it aloud to students) and discuss similarities between *Bridge to Terabithia* and this book.

Writing

Have students write an essay about friendship. Some topic ideas follow:

- Describe in detail your best friend, citing examples that show loyalty and trustworthiness.

- Henry David Thoreau wrote, "Could a greater miracle take place than for us to look through each other's eyes for an instant?" Explain how this quote applies to Leslie and Jess, giving specific examples.

- Become Leslie for a moment. Write down what really happened at the creek right before she drowned.

- Rabbi Loew wrote, "In some special way each person completes the universe." Explain how Leslie completed Jess's personal universe. Then reflect whether you think this statement is true for all people.

Video

PBS Wonderworks produced *Bridge to Terabithia* as a 50-minute film for television. Although many parts from the book are missing or changed, the two characters of Leslie and Jess are very well portrayed. Having students watch the film and note differences and similarities between it and the book could be beneficial.

Park's Quest

by Katherine Paterson

Synopsis

Eleven-year-old Parkington Waddell Broughton V really knows two things about his father: Park was named for him and he was killed in Vietnam when Park was a baby. But when the Vietnam Memorial is dedicated in Washington, D.C., Park's interest in his father is heightened. Reluctantly, Park's mother agrees to let Park spend some time with his father's side of the family in rural Virginia. There, for the first time, he meets his invalid grandfather, his uncle, and the Vietnamese girl, Thahn. Park's quest jumps from pursuing reassuring fantasies to facing stark reality.

Vocabulary

CHAPTER 1

1. avenging
2. peril
3. quest
4. villain
5. deceased

References:
- King Arthur
- Morgan le Fay
- Camelot
- Gareth

CHAPTER 2

1. exuberant
2. mischievous
3. bantering
4. servitude

References:
- Sir Gawain
- Conrad
- The Green Chapel

CHAPTER 3

1. crevice
2. granite
3. bounty

References:
- Holy Grail
- Holy Vessel

CHAPTER 4

1. reprimand
2. rural

CHAPTER 5

1. conjured
2. amber
3. davenport
4. chagrin
5. chivalry
6. contemplation
7. chalice

Reference:
- Round Table

CHAPTER 6

1. feigns
2. foes
3. refugees
4. spigot

Reference:
- Lancelot

CHAPTER 7

1. tenants
2. spitfire
3. placidly

CHAPTER 8

1. invalid
2. testy
3. temperamental

CHAPTER 9

1. namesake
2. wail
3. wretched

CHAPTER 10

1. heathen

CHAPTER 11

1. besmirched
2. afghan

CHAPTER 12

1. mollify
2. hermit
3. rogue

Reference:
- confusion of crows

CHAPTER 13

1. festered
2. ominous
3. tactic

CHAPTER 14

1. saucy

Park's Quest—Chapters 1–7

Vocabulary: Using the vocabulary list given below, fill in the blanks with appropriate words.

granite	refugees	conjured	King Arthur
Camelot	reprimand	rural	Conrad
quest	deceased		

1. Over the years, Park had _____ up an image of the perfect father.

2. Park was on his own personal _____ when he went to the Vietnam Memorial.

3. He had seen the word _____ after his father's name and it always saddened him.

4. When Park arrived home, his mother did not _____ him but she seemed upset.

5. Park's fantasies included the tales of _____ .

6. Park's grandfather and family lived in _____ Virginia.

7. His father's name was carved on the _____ stone.

8. His father had a book written by _____ which Park tried to read.

9. King Arthur was the ruler of the kingdom of _____ .

10. When Park first met Thahn he wondered if she was one of the many _____ who had come to the U.S.

True/False: Write *true* or *false* for each of the following statements, using your knowledge of the vocabulary words and the story.

1. _____ Park imagined himself living like one of the knights in King Arthur's time.

2. _____ Park was on a quest for the Holy Grail.

3. _____ The Vietnam War Memorial is located in New York.

4. _____ Park's uncle seemed like a villain to Park.

5. _____ A "quest" is usually a short journey.

Short Answer: Using complete sentences, write the answers to the following questions.

1. What do you think is Park's quest?

2. Describe at least two ways in which his grandfather's home in Virginia is different from his own outside Washington.

Park's Quest—Chapters 8–14

Multiple Choice: Choose the one best answer to complete each of the following statements. Write the letter of that choice in the blank.

1. _____ Park has gone to visit his grandfather who lives in   (a) Connecticut   (b) South Carolina   (c) Virginia   (d) Tennessee.

2. _____ He is surprised to find out that   (a) Frank also fought in the Vietnam War   (b) his grandfather owns a farm   (c) Frank married a Vietnamese woman   (d) Thahn is 10 or 11 years old.

3. _____ Mrs. Davenport is   (a) Park's teacher from school   (b) the therapist who works with Park's grandfather three days a week   (c) Frank's wife   (d) the caretaker for Park's grandfather.

4. _____ Park's favorite nickname for Thahn is   (a) geek   (b) birdbrain   (c) brat   (d) Tom.

5. _____ Park is very excited when his uncle   (a) asks him to do chores   (b) teaches him how to shoot a rifle   (c) takes him to town   (d) introduces him to his grandfather.

6. _____ One of the best words to describe Thahn would be   (a) considerate   (b) serious   (c) comical   (d) rude.

7. _____ Park gets upset with his mother because   (a) she wants to start dating again   (b) she never told him anything about his father's family   (c) she never wants him to shoot a gun   (d) she won't give him any extra spending money.

8. _____ Park sees his grandfather for the first time   (a) on the porch   (b) when he first arrives at the farm   (c) when he goes into the old man's bedroom at night   (d) at the springhouse, late at night.

9. _____ At the springhouse early in the morning, Park is surprised   (a) to find Frank there   (b) to hear Thahn crying   (c) to find a picture of his father there   (d) to find Jupe there.

10. _____ At the end, the "grail" is shared between Park, Thahn, and   (a) the grandfather   (b) Frank   (c) Jupe   (d) the crow.

Vocabulary: Using your knowledge of the vocabulary words and the story, answer the following questions.

1. Who was a little "temperamental"? _____

2. Who was an invalid? _____

3. How did Park mollify Thahn about the crow? _____

_____

4. Who did Park call "the little heathen"? _____

5. For the old man, what has festered in his heart for many years? _____

_____

Name: _____ Date: _____

Final Test
Park's Quest

Multiple Response: Choose as many answers as are needed in order to complete each statement correctly. This means you may choose only one letter, or as many as all four.

1. _____ Park's mother (a) didn't want to really talk to Park about his father (b) decided to join Park in Virginia (c) was named Randy (d) said she couldn't forgive Park's father.

2. _____ Park was surprised about his grandfather when (a) Park saw he was an invalid (b) Park realized how angry he was that Park had come to visit (c) he actually smiled after his wild wheelchair ride (d) he told Park he was glad for this visit.

3. _____ Mrs. Davenport (a) is the grandfather's caretaker (b) is Thahn's grandmother (c) says she can't understand why Frank married a Vietnamese woman (d) thinks it would be better if the old man died.

4. _____ References are made to (a) Queen Elizabeth I (b) the French Revolution (c) King Arthur (d) the Holy Grail.

5. _____ Park likes his Uncle Frank because (a) Frank puts Thahn in her place and doesn't put up with her sass (b) Frank taught him how to shoot (c) Frank taught him how to drive a car (d) Frank showed him all the old pictures of Park's dad.

6. _____ At the beginning of the book (a) Veterans' Day was about to be celebrated in the Washington, D.C., area (b) Park and his mother go to the Vietnam Memorial (c) Park gets a letter from his uncle, asking him to visit (d) Park wants to know more about his father.

7. _____ Thahn and Park are alike in that they (a) both had the same father (b) want to know more about their past (c) both had to learn an additional language besides English (d) hate Mrs. Davenport's food.

8. _____ The springhouse (a) is Frank's favorite place (b) is where Park's father is buried (c) is Thahn's favorite place (d) has fresh, pure water to drink.

9. _____ On his visit to Virginia, Park finds out that (a) Thahn is his half sister (b) his father had been AWOL at the time of his death (c) his parents had been divorced (d) he has an uncle.

10. _____ In the last chapter of the book (a) Thahn's baby brother is born (b) the grandfather dies (c) Park leaves the farm (d) Park tells his mother everything he knows.

Essay: Write a complete paragraph to answer the following question.

How do you think Park's life will be different after his visit to Virginia?

Answer Key

Park's Quest (*Worksheet, Chapters 1–7*)

Vocabulary

1. conjured
2. quest
3. deceased
4. reprimand
5. King Arthur
6. rural
7. granite
8. Conrad
9. Camelot
10. refugees

True/False

1. true
2. false
3. false
4. false
5. false

Short Answer (Answers will vary.)

1. Park wants to know more about his father. His quest, therefore, would include anything that would help fill in the missing pieces—the trip to the Vietnam Memorial, visiting his grandfather's place, talking with Frank. His quest to know more about his father will undoubtedly turn into a quest to help Park define his own identity better.

2. His grandfather's house is huge—three stories high with porches all around. There is lots of land and it's very green and beautiful. In contrast, his "house" outside Washington, D.C., is just a small apartment that Park and his mother share. Every night Park has to make up his bed on the couch because he has no bedroom of his own.

Park's Quest (*Worksheet, Chapters 8–14*)

Multiple Choice

1. c		6. d	
2. c		7. b	
3. d		8. c	
4. a		9. b	
5. b		10. a	

Vocabulary

1. Thahn
2. the grandfather
3. He told her that the crow was only wounded, not dead.
4. Thahn
5. He thought he was in some way responsible for his son's death.

Final Test

Multiple Response

1. a, c, d
2. a, c
3. a, c, d
4. c, d
5. a, b
6. a, d
7. a, b, d
8. c, d
9. a, c, d
10. a, d

Essay (Answers will vary.)

Knowing that he now has a sister will change Park's life forever. He now is part of a family and he won't feel so isolated. He may even become more sensitive to Thahn's feelings and his mother's pain. Finally, this might be a time for healing for the mother as she and Park communicate more openly.

Extension Activities

Park's Quest

Discussion

CHAPTER 1
1. What does Park fantasize about? What does this tell us about him?
2. Even though it seems as though Park doesn't know much about his father, what are all the things he does know?

CHAPTER 2
1. What kinds of books does Park hate? Why?
2. Why did Park read the book by Conrad?

CHAPTER 3
1. How do we know that Park's mother never got along with her in-laws?

CHAPTER 4
1. What mistake did Park make about the "hired man"?
2. What surprises him about his grandfather?

CHAPTER 5
1. On his first afternoon at his grandfather's place, what special place does he find?

CHAPTER 6
1. Why don't Thahn and Park get along at first?
2. How does Park feel out of place here in Virginia?

CHAPTER 7
1. What new information does Park find out from Mrs. Davenport?
2. How is Park's mother trying to protect him?

CHAPTER 8
1. Why do you think Thahn was crying in the springhouse?

CHAPTER 9
1. What kind of person is Frank? Is he good for Park? Why?
2. What does Park discover that night?

CHAPTER 10
1. What is Park's first reaction when he finds out his parents were divorced?
2. How does Frank show his sensitivity and understanding for his nephew?

CHAPTER 11
1. The title of this chapter is "The King Goes Riding." Who is the king and how does he go riding?
2. What did Park discover about Thahn? About his grandfather?

CHAPTER 12
1. Why did Park feel good about himself as he walked to the field with the gun?
2. Why would Thahn be so upset about the death of one crow?

CHAPTER 13
1. How are Park's mother and Thahn's mother similar?
2. What does the statement "Park had thought it was death that could not be forgiven, and all the time it had been life" mean?

CHAPTER 14
1. Who is in the company of the Grail at the end?
2. What does Park realize about his grandfather?

(continued)

49

Reading

1. As an introduction to *Park's Quest* there is an excellent picture book by Eve Bunting called *The Wall*. The illustrations by Ronald Himler and the story make it very easy to understand what it must be like to go to the Vietnam War Memorial for the first time.

2. For factual information about the dedication of the Vietnam War Memorial there is an article with wonderful pictures in the May 1985 issue of *National Geographic*. This article ties in perfectly with the first few chapters of *Park's Quest*, because it is the same Dedication Day as Park experiences in the book.

3. There are two excellent young adult books about the Vietnam War: *Fallen Angels* by Walter Dean Myers and *Young Man in Vietnam* by Charles Coe.

4. Katherine Paterson has written several high-quality books for young people. Following are some of them:

   * *Bridge to Terabithia*   ** *Rebels of the Heavenly Kingdom*
   Come Sing, Jimmy Jo   *The Master Puppeteer*
   The Great Gilly Hopkins   *Of Nightingales That Weep*
   Jacob Have I Loved

   * covered in this volume
   ** covered in Volume II of this series

5. In the book *Eight Plus One* by Robert Cormier there is a short story entitled "The Moustache." The story tells of a grandson who goes to visit his invalid grandmother in a nursing home. The story is a nice complement for *Park's Quest* when Park meets his invalid grandfather for the first time. The story could be read aloud with discussion afterwards.

6. There are several good books about immigrants and the special problems they face in the U.S. To help the class (or individual students) understand Thahn's situation better, share some of this information. A book such as *New Americans: An Oral History* by Al Santoli is an excellent source.

7. The young adult books *A Boat to Nowhere* and *A Long Way From Home*, both written by Maureen Crane Wartski, tell the story of Vietnamese Mai who escapes from Vietnam by boat. The first book deals with her escape to freedom; the second one deals with Mai's adjustment to America. The problems a Vietnamese refugee has when adopted by a non-Vietnamese family are described in the young adult novel *Promises to Come* by Jim Heneghan.

8. Many students love to hear about the tales of King Arthur and Camelot. Following are brief descriptions of the references to Arthurian legend that appear in *Park's Quest*:

   • King Arthur—legendary king of Great Britain; creator of the Round Table, knights, "might for right"

(continued)

- Morgan le Fay—half-sister of King Arthur; usually an evil sorceress
- Gareth and Sir Gawain—knights of King Arthur
- Camelot—King Arthur's kingdom
- Holy Grail (Holy Vessel)—the cup that Jesus drank from at the Last Supper. (In Arthurian legend only one without sin could look upon the Holy Grail, and this was Lancelot's son, Sir Galahad.)
- Green Chapel—one of the places associated with Sir Gawain in stories about him
- Lancelot—the greatest of all of King Arthur's knights

Encourage interested students to further their reading about King Arthur. There are many books, all written at different levels of difficulty, to enlighten students about this never-ending legend.

Writing

1. Pair up boy/girl teams and have them write imaginary letters that Park and Thahn might have written to each other in the following year.

2. If Park had been assigned a theme his first week of school titled "My Summer Vacation," what would he have written? Tell students to become Park and write that theme.

Art

1. The competition for the design of the Vietnam War Memorial was open to anyone who wanted to enter. Decide on some international recent event (for example, the fall of the Berlin Wall, the Gulf War) or a local recent event and have students design their own memorial to it. Display all of the designs and discuss the feasibility, the materials that would have to be used, the cost, and so forth. If you live in a city with a lot of statues or memorials, you could discuss these with the class. Time (and new information) changes our perspective about memorials. Discuss with your class if any memorials should be changed, amended, or completely torn down. What should be the criteria for a memorial to be erected?

2. Have a student illustrate certain scenes from the book, such as the springhouse, the wheelchair ride, the house in Virginia, or Park standing at the Wall.

Drama

1. Many of the scenes between Park and Thahn lend themselves easily to play format. Have students write out a scene and either read through it in front of the class or act it out.

2. Park and his mother need to have a long conversation about all that Park has learned this summer. Have students pretend that Park has arrived home and he and his mother have this conversation. Tell students to write the scene that might happen and act it out for the class.

The Pinballs

by Betsy Byars

Synopsis

For their own separate reasons Carlie, Thomas J, and Harvey have been sent to the same foster home. Carlie says that like pinballs, they are out of control and cannot help each other. But she learns that she does have the power to help someone else, and that some decisions are within her control.

Vocabulary

CHAPTER 1

1. essay
2. foster
3. resented
4. concussion
5. collapsed
6. stabilizes

CHAPTER 2

1. forge

CHAPTER 3

1. deaf
2. bushel
3. twinge

CHAPTER 4

1. technique
2. admired
3. vaccine

CHAPTER 5

1. commune
2. yoga
3. cathedral
4. gnarled
5. maharishna

CHAPTER 6

1. groove

CHAPTER 7

1. punctuation
2. appendectomy
3. majorette
4. incisions

CHAPTER 8

1. puberty

CHAPTER 9

1. addicted
2. strays

CHAPTER 10

NONE

CHAPTER 11

1. abandoned

CHAPTER 12

1. guinea pig

CHAPTER 13

1. valuable
2. rhythmic

CHAPTER 14

1. criticize

CHAPTER 15

1. fidget
2. abruptly

CHAPTER 16

NONE

CHAPTER 17

1. laid-out

CHAPTER 18

1. mute
2. sulk
3. feeble

CHAPTER 19

1. agonized

CHAPTERS 20 & 21

NONE

CHAPTER 22

1. cahoots

CHAPTER 23

1. spigot
2. commotion

CHAPTERS 24–26

NONE

The Pinballs—Chapters 1–13

Vocabulary: Fill in the blanks with appropriate words taken from the vocabulary lists for Chapters 1–13.

1. Carlie was sent to live with the Masons until her home situation _____ .

2. Thomas J was walking behind the twins carrying a _____ basket when they slipped and fell.

3. Harvey's mother left three years ago to live in a _____ with nineteen other people.

4. Number one on Harvey's list of "Bad Things that Have Happened to Me" was his _____ .

5. Harvey won a prize for his _____ on "Why I Am Proud to Be an American."

6. Thomas J stood there imagining himself as an _____ child in just a diaper and shirt.

7. Harvey once bought himself a _____ for Christmas.

8. Harvey said he was _____ to Kentucky Fried Chicken.

9. Even though Carlie went to _____ clinic she shouldn't try out because of her grades.

10. When Carlie wrote a letter to her mom she didn't bother with _____ .

11. Carlie thought it was too bad there wasn't a _____ for homesickness.

12. Harvey looked at his white casts and wished he had thought to _____ some names on them.

13. Carlie's stepfather hit her so hard she had a _____ .

14. Harvey was placed in the _____ home until his dad could control his drinking.

15. Thomas J _____ Carlie and wanted her to like him.

Short Answer: Answer the following questions in one or two complete sentences.

1. In what way does Carlie mean that they are like pinballs?

2. Mrs. Mason told Carlie that things hadn't worked out the way she had planned. What did she mean?

Name: _____   Date: _____

The Pinballs—Chapters 14–26

Vocabulary: Fill in the blanks with appropriate words taken from the vocabulary lists for Chapters 14–26.

1. After the accident both twins seemed weak and _____ .

2. Harvey was too nervous to _____ while he waited for his father.

3. Harvey couldn't imagine his mother allowing anyone to _____ her.

4. Carlie and Thomas J were in _____ about getting the puppy for Harvey.

5. When Harvey finally cried, it was like turning on a _____ .

6. Harvey was just sitting there, not pouting or _____ .

7. Mr. Mason said he remembered the first funeral he attended where someone was _____ at home.

8. Carlie got up _____ and went into the house when Harvey's father arrived.

9. Even though the nurse heard all the _____ , she acted as if it didn't matter.

10. Harvey sat _____ (ly) at dinner and didn't respond to Carlie's jibes.

True/False: Write *true* or *false* for each of the following statements.

1. _____ Carlie went to the library to find an article about becoming a majorette.

2. _____ Harvey used to think his mother wrote letters to him from the commune.

3. _____ The twins were named after Teddy Roosevelt.

4. _____ Carlie's favorite books were about nurses around the world.

5. _____ Harvey wrote to his mother at the commune.

6. _____ Mr. Mason's own son was away in the army.

7. _____ The twins died the same day.

8. _____ It was difficult for both Mr. Mason and Thomas J to say "I love you."

9. _____ Harvey had to stay in the hospital because his leg was infected.

10. _____ The nurse made Carlie and Thomas J take the puppy outside.

Name: _____   Date: _____

Final Test
The Pinballs

Character Identification: Write the character's letter in the blank next to each description of that character. You may use some letters more than once.

(a) Harvey   (c) Thomas J   (e) Carlie   (g) Mrs. Mason

(b) Nurse   (d) Benson twins   (f) Mr. Mason

1. _____ Used to yelling to be heard.

2. _____ Was addicted to Kentucky Fried Chicken.

3. _____ Had on a Snoopy shirt when found.

4. _____ Thought maybe Carlie could help Harvey.

5. _____ Said that the injuries were caused by playing football.

6. _____ Went to Majorette Clinic.

7. _____ Made lists.

8. _____ Felt terrible if someone said something nice or polite.

9. _____ Had broken hips.

10. _____ Felt the habit to pray was strong.

11. _____ Once had a guinea pig named Snowball.

12. _____ Was abandoned as a baby.

13. _____ Favorite book was *Hong Kong Nurse.*

14. _____ Mother lives in a commune.

15. _____ Didn't think of the children as "strays."

16. _____ Don't believe in candy or soda pop.

17. _____ Wrote an essay about being a proud American.

18. _____ Thought "I can always run away."

19. _____ Favorite Bible story was about baby Moses.

20. _____ Once had an appendectomy.

21. _____ It took five years to tell his wife, "I love you."

22. _____ Said, "I never give up on anybody I like."

23. _____ Read somewhere that everybody will be famous for **fifteen minutes.**

24. _____ Said "If I had seen that puppy I would have to send him out **this minute.**"

25. _____ She had pictures of the children on the mantel.

Answer Key

The Pinballs (*Worksheet, Chapters 1–13*)

Vocabulary

1. stabilizes	6. abandoned	11. vaccine
2. bushel	7. guinea pig	12. forge
3. commune	8. addicted	13. concussion
4. appendectomy	9. majorette	14. foster
5. essay	10. punctuation	15. admired

Short Answer

1. They have no control over events in their lives and cannot be helped by others.

2. Mrs. Mason used to want children of her own, but now feels good about being a foster parent.

The Pinballs (*Worksheet, Chapters 14–26*)

Vocabulary

1. feeble	6. sulking
2. fidget	7. laid-out
3. criticize	8. abruptly
4. cahoots	9. commotion
5. spigot	10. mutely

True/False

1. false	6. false
2. true	7. false
3. false	8. true
4. true	9. true
5. true	10. false

Final Test

Character Identification

1. c	6. e	11. a	16. d	21. f
2. a	7. a	12. c	17. a	22. e
3. c	8. e	13. e	18. e	23. a
4. g	9. d	14. a	19. c	24. b
5. a	10. c	15. g	20. a	25. g

Extension Activities

The Pinballs

Discussion

CHAPTERS 1–2

1. Why were each of the children assigned to foster care?

2. Why doesn't Carlie believe Harvey's story about a football accident?

CHAPTERS 3–4

1. How did Thomas J get his name?

2. What do you think it was like for Thomas J living with the twins?

CHAPTERS 5–6

1. Why did Harvey's mother leave?

2. How does Carlie think the children are like pinballs?

CHAPTERS 7–8

1. What does Carlie's letter reveal to the audience about her home life?

2. What kinds of lists does Harvey make?

CHAPTERS 9–10

1. Why was Harvey "addicted" to Kentucky Fried Chicken?

2. Why didn't Thomas J bring the twins anything in the hospital?

CHAPTERS 11–12

1. What did Thomas J imagine about himself at the farm?

2. Why did Harvey's father get rid of the guinea pig?

CHAPTERS 13–14

1. Carlie says, "Life is really unfair." What does she mean?

2. Why did Harvey come to the library?

CHAPTERS 15–16

1. Why is Harvey worried about his fifteen minutes?

2. What does Harvey learn about his mother?

CHAPTERS 17–18

1. What do we learn about Mr. Mason in this chapter?

2. How does Mrs. Mason think Carlie has helped Harvey?

CHAPTERS 19–20

1. How does Carlie discover that Harvey's leg is infected?

2. What does Carlie think about Harvey's father's problem?

CHAPTERS 21–22

1. How was their visit to Harvey a failure?

2. What is Carlie's good idea?

CHAPTERS 23–24

1. Why does the nurse allow them to stay with the puppy?

2. How does Thomas J get a birthday?

CHAPTERS 25–26

1. Why is this haircut different for Thomas J?

2. How has Carlie changed?

(continued)

The Pinballs (continued)

Reading

1. Other books written by Betsy Byars include the following:

After the Goat Man	*The Night Swimmers*	*Trouble River*
Cracker Jackson	*The Not-Just-Anybody Family*	*The TV Kid*
The Cybil War	*Rama, the Gypsy Cat*	*Two Thousand Pound Goldfish*
The House of Wings	*The Summer of the Swans*	*The Winged Colt of Casa Mia*
The Midnight Fox		

2. One of the themes of *The Pinballs* is adjustment to a new home. These other young adult books have this same theme of moving to a new home and trying to fit in.

The Broccoli Tapes by Jan Slepian   * *A Solitary Blue* by Cynthia Voight
Kentucky Daughter by Carol J. Scott   *The Doll in the Garden* by Mary Downing Hahn
The Atami Dragons by David Klass   *Vision Quest* by Pamela F. Service
Home Before Dark by Sue Ellen Bridges   * covered in Volume II of this series

3. Following are some excellent young adult books concerning the consequences of child abuse:

The Lottery Rose by Irene Hunt   *Paper Knife* by Marc Talbert
I Never Asked You to Understand Me   * *The Creep* by Susan Dodson
    by Barthe DeClements   * covered in Volume II of this series

Writing

Have students write the following sequels to the book:

(a) Mrs. Mason said that many of the foster children she helped now write letters to her. Imagine that when Carlie, Thomas J, and Harvey are twenty, they each write to Mrs. Mason. What would they say?

(b) Thomas J was assigned to the foster home until such time as his identity could be established or adoptive parents found. Imagine Thomas J's history and establish his identity. Write about how he was lost or abandoned. Or write about an adoptive family situation.

Research

Most communities have foster parent families that are supervised by social service agencies. Contact the social service agency in your area to discover the requirements for becoming foster parents.

Art

Create a family tree for the characters in this book. Have Mr. and Mrs. Mason as the trunk and the three children as branches. Record important characteristics and events on "leaves" that attach to the appropriate branch.

Drama

Write in play form an imaginary last chapter for this book in which all the characters say good-bye.

Sarah, Plain and Tall

by Patricia MacLachlan

Synopsis

Anna and her brother, Caleb, miss their mother and all the love she added to their lives. So their papa places an advertisement in a newspaper hoping to find a new wife willing to share his home and family. Sarah Elisabeth Wheaton answers the ad and fills the emptiness in their lives. Although she misses her home in Maine, she learns that she would miss this new family even more if she didn't stay.

Vocabulary

(Includes regional terms and period vernacular that might need explanation or clarification.)

CHAPTER 1

1. dusk
2. hearthstone
3. marble slab kitchen table
4. prairie
5. feisty

CHAPTER 2

1. "the colors of the sea"
2. "the color of fog"
3. flounder (fish)
4. seabass (fish)
5. whales
6. seabirds
7. cow pond
8. bonnet

CHAPTER 3

1. Indian paintbrush (flower)
2. blue-eyed grass
3. woodchuck
4. marsh hawk
5. windmill
6. Russian Olive tree
7. moonsnail shell
8. blue flax (flower)

CHAPTER 4

1. scallop
2. razor clam
3. oyster
4. clover
5. violets (flower)
6. bride's bonnet (flower)
7. goldenrod (flower)
8. asters (flower)
9. woolly ragwort (flower)
10. Kittiwake gull (bird)
11. seals
12. meadowlark (bird)

CHAPTER 5

1. dune
2. mica (stone)

CHAPTER 6

1. plow
2. sums
3. tumbleweeds
4. petticoat
5. killdeer (bird)

CHAPTER 7

1. daisies (flower)
2. zinnias (flower)
3. marigold (flower)
4. dahlias (flower)
5. columbine (flower)
6. feverfew (flower)
7. nasturtium (flower)

CHAPTER 8

1. carpenter
2. squall

CHAPTER 9

NONE

Name: _____   Date: _____

Sarah, Plain and Tall—Chapters 1–3

Cloze Exercise: Using your knowledge of the book, fill in the blanks with appropriate names or common words that would make sense within the context of the story.

The mother of Anna and Caleb died the morning after Caleb was born. It took Anna

(1) _____ whole days to learn to (2) _____ him. Now the

children miss the (3) _____ their mother used to sing. Caleb asked Papa why

he didn't (4) _____ anymore and Papa said "I've (5) _____

the old songs." But Papa hoped there was a way to (6) _____ the old songs.

He placed an (7) _____ in the newspaper in hopes of finding someone to be

his new (8) _____ and mother for his children.

(9) _____ Elisabeth Wheaton answered the (10) _____ .

She lived in (11) _____ with her older (12) _____ who was

about to (13) _____ . She felt it was time for her to (14) _____ .

She wrote Anna's family that she was strong but not mild (15) _____ . She also

said that she owned a (16) _____ . After Papa read her

(17) _____ aloud to the (18) _____ , Caleb said he hoped she

could sing.

That winter Sarah answered (19) _____ from each member of the

(20) _____ . She assured Anna that she could (21) _____ hair.

She wrote Caleb that she could keep a (22) _____ going all night but wasn't

sure if she (23) _____ . To Papa she accepted an invitation to come for a

(24) _____ and that yes, she could (25) _____ .

Papa got dressed up to pick Sarah up from the (26) _____ . The children

recognized her by her yellow (27) _____ .

Name: _____ Date: _____

Sarah, Plain and Tall—Chapters 4–9

Cloze Exercise: Using your knowledge of the book, fill in the blanks with appropriate names or common words that would make sense within the context of the story.

Although Sarah missed the sea, she found new things to love out on the prairie. She picked

lots of (1)_____ and named the (2)_____ and chickens.

Caleb created (3)_____ for her from a (4)_____ that they

could (5)_____ down. The cow pond became the (6)_____

in miniature.

When the (7)_____ came over to help with the (8)_____ ,

Sarah and Maggie became friends right away. (9)_____ confided that she

missed the hills of Tennessee. Sarah said she missed the sea and (10)_____ old

(11)_____ . Maggie brought plants for Sarah to start a (12)_____

and she encouraged Sarah to learn to (13)_____ the wagon.

The next day Sarah was eager to learn to drive, but Papa said that first he should fix the

(14)_____ before the (15)_____ came. Luckily, Sarah was an

experienced (16)_____ and they safely survived the squall.

Papa kept his promise and taught Sarah to (17)_____ the wagon. The next

day Sarah put on her blue (18)_____ and drove away. The children were afraid

she would not (19)_____ . They knew she was lonely for the sea, but didn't

want her to (20)_____ .

Sarah did come back. She had gone into town and bought three colored

(21)_____ the (22)_____ of the sea. Sarah told Anna and

Caleb that she would always miss the sea, but she would miss the (23)_____

more.

Anna knew there would be a (24)_____ soon.

Name: _____   Date: _____

Final Test
Sarah, Plain and Tall

Regional Identification: Decide which of the following terms are identified with Sarah's seaside home or Anna's prairie home. List the terms in the correct column.

wooly ragwort   razor clam   blue-eyed grass
bride's bonnet   cow pond   whales
Russian Olive trees   fields   flounder
dunes   fog   corn
Kittiwake gull   meadowlark   seals
windmill   moonsnail   scallops
tumbleweed   Indian paintbrush

SARAH'S WORLD	ANNA'S WORLD

Short Answer: Answer each of the following questions in one or two complete sentences.

1. Why does Sarah scatter the curls after haircuts?

2. What story did Caleb like Anna to tell him over and over?

3. Why did Sarah decide it was time for her to move away from Maine?

4. Why didn't the housekeeper that Papa hired work out?

Answer Key

Sarah, Plain and Tall (Worksheet, Chapters 1–3)

Cloze Exercise

1. three	7. advertisement (ad)	13. marry	19. letters	25. sing
2. love	8. wife	14. move	20. family	26. train
3. songs	9. Sarah	15. mannered	21. braid	27. bonnet
4. sing	10. ad	16. cat	22. fire	
5. forgotten	11. Maine	17. letter	23. snored	
6. remember	12. brother	18. children	24. visit	

Sarah, Plain and Tall (Worksheet, Chapters 4–9)

Cloze Exercise

1. flowers	6. sea	11. aunts	16. carpenter	21. pencils
2. sheep	7. neighbors	12. garden	17. drive	22. colors
3. dune	8. plowing	13. drive	18. dress	23. children
4. haystack	9. Maggie	14. roof	19. return	24. wedding
5. slide	10. three	15. storm	20. leave	

Final Test

Regional Identification

SARAH'S WORLD		ANNA'S WORLD	
woolly ragwort	moonsnail	bride's bonnet	fields
dunes	whales	Russian Olive trees	meadowlark
Kittiwake gull	flounder	windmill	Indian paintbrush
razor clam	seals	tumbleweed	blue-eyed grass
fog	scallops	cow pond	corn

Short Answer

1. Sarah scatters the curls so the birds can use them for their nests.

2. Caleb loves to hear the story of the day he was born.

3. Her brother was about to be married, and she didn't want to intrude on them.

4. She couldn't keep a fire going all night and she snored.

Extension Activities

Sarah, Plain and Tall

Discussion

CHAPTER 1

1. Why do you think it took Anna three days to love Caleb?

CHAPTER 2

1. How does Caleb react to his letter from Sarah?

CHAPTER 3

1. What does Anna wish for Sarah? Why?

CHAPTER 4

1. What kinds of things are Sarah and the children learning from each other?

CHAPTER 5

1. What made Sarah slide down the dune?

2. What comment made by Sarah gives Caleb hope?

CHAPTER 6

1. This chapter says that "Sarah was happy." What kinds of things are making her happy?

CHAPTER 7

1. What characteristics do Sarah and Maggie share?

2. What good piece of advice did Maggie leave Sarah?

CHAPTER 8

1. The children and Papa learn a lot about Sarah in this chapter. What do they learn?

CHAPTER 9

1. Why didn't Papa ask Sarah where she was going?

2. Why does Caleb think Sarah will leave?

Reading

1. Other books by Patricia MacLachlan include:

   Arthur, For the Very First Time   *Tomorrow's Wizard*
   Through Grandpa's Eyes   *Seven Kisses in a Row*
   Cassie Binegar   *Unclaimed Treasures*
   Mama One, Mama Two   *The Facts and Fictions of Minna Pratt*

2. Some other books depicting prairie life during this period are:

   Prairie Songs by Pam Conrad   *Honey Girl* by Madge Harrah
   My Daniel by Pam Conrad   *Save Queen of Sheba* by Louise Moeri
   The American Girls Collection—the   *The Little House on the Prairie* series by
       Kirsten books by Janet Shaw   Laura Ingalls Wilder
   Beyond the Divide by Kathryn Lasky   *The Orphan Train Quartet* by Joan Low-
   A Gathering of Days by Joan Blos   ery Nixon

(continued)

Writing

1. *Sarah, Plain and Tall* was based on a real event in the author's family history. Have students write in story format about one event in their own family history.

2. *Sequel:* Have students write a sequel to this book from the perspective of Anna's grandchild. Did Sarah and Papa have any more children? Did Sarah ever bring the children to Maine for a visit? Did the family save all the letters they exchanged?

3. *Letters:* Assign students to write letters from Sarah to her brother, William, describing her new home and family.

4. *Diary Entry:* Have students imagine that on the day Sarah decides she is going to stay, she writes about her decision in her diary. What would the entry say?

Research

1. Students may enjoy researching information on mail-order brides. When did this practice begin? Is it going on today?

2. Sarah sent the children a book about seabirds to show them what she could see in Maine every day. Have students research the birds that live by the sea, comparing and constrasting them to the birds that live on the prairie.

3. Many plants and flowers are mentioned in this book. Have students research the flowers listed in the Vocabulary section and identify which would be most likely to be found on the prairie or by the sea (or both). Students might also want to make a collection of flowers found in their own region.

Video

"Hallmark Hall of Fame" presented *Sarah, Plain and Tall* as a television special in 1991. The film is not available commercially as of this writing.

Art

1. Have students research and illustrate the different flowers and/or birds mentioned in the Vocabulary section. Students interested in flowers could create a flower collage bouquet for Sarah's wedding. Students interested in birds could make a seabird collage poster, or a prairie-bird collage poster.

2. Have students illustrate Anna's home and the surrounding area. The illustrations should include the barn, the hay dune, the fields, the cow pond, and the garden.

3. Anna mentioned that in Sarah's guest room, the bed was covered by a quilt. Quilting was a popular art form of this period. Students may be interested in making a class patchwork quilt out of paper. Have students look at various quilt designs and then each make their own "square."

Sounder

by William H. Armstrong

Synopsis

A man is arrested for stealing food for his hungry family. The man's son tries to find his father at the numerous work camps throughout the South only to meet cruelty and prejudice at every turn. But, during one journey, he meets a teacher who becomes his friend and guide. Tying the story together is Sounder, the coon hunting dog, who refuses to give up.

Vocabulary

CHAPTER 1
1. successive
2. quarry
3. addled
4. coverlet
5. seep
6. spires
7. whetstone

CHAPTER 2
1. ashen
2. mongrel
3. clammy
4. constrained
5. plaintive
6. floundering

CHAPTER 3
1. skittish
2. haunches
3. pallet
4. visualize

CHAPTER 4
1. poultice
2. carcass
3. quiver

CHAPTER 5
1. famished
2. remote

CHAPTER 6
1. sneer
2. lowlands

CHAPTER 7
1. compulsion
2. rivulets
3. gyrations
4. glee
5. gaunt
6. defiant
7. malicious
8. animosity
9. jeered
10. cistern
11. sanctuary
12. lean
13. mellow

CHAPTER 8
1. drought
2. mimicked
3. rhythmic
4. askew
5. sultry
6. flex
7. withered
8. crescent

Name: _____   Date: _____

Sounder—Chapters 1-4

Sequencing: Number from 1 to 7 in the correct order in which these events happened in the book.

_____ The father is taken away by the deputies.

_____ The children smell ham and sausage cooking for breakfast.

_____ Sounder is shot.

_____ The boy takes a cake to his father.

_____ The mother returns the stolen food.

_____ The father goes out at night without Sounder.

_____ The father tells the boy not to return anymore.

Character Identification: Write the character's letter in the blank next to each description of that character. You may use a letter more than once.

(A) The boy   (b) The father   (c) The mother

1. _____ Says he's about the same age as Sounder.

2. _____ To Sounder, is Master.

3. _____ Hums when worried.

4. _____ Picks kernels of walnuts and sells them.

5. _____ The oldest child in the family.

6. _____ Tells the children stories from the Bible.

7. _____ Wants to learn to read more than anything else.

8. _____ Chained up by sheriff.

9. _____ Tells son not to try to find Sounder: "Creatures like to die alone."

10. _____ Bought bottle of vanilla flavoring.

11. _____ Hates the red-faced man who destroyed the cake.

12. _____ Will send word with the visiting preacher.

13. _____ Arrested for stealing.

14. _____ Said, "Night loneliness is part fearing."

15. _____ Looks all over for the wounded Sounder but cannot find him.

Name: _____ Date: _____

Sounder—Chapters 5–8

Vocabulary: Fill in the blanks with an appropriate choice from the list below:

sanctuary   defiant   famished
cistern   lean   mellow
drought   withered   sneer
compulsion

1. The guard gave a _____ as he hit the boy's knuckles with the iron pipe.

2. The _____ of the summer months had left all the fields bare.

3. After returning from the work camps, his father's body _____ more and more each day.

4. Some kind of _____ kept the boy searching for his father.

5. He went to the _____ beside the school to wash his hands.

6. The _____ eyes of the teacher made him seem more trusting.

7. When the guard hit him, he had maintained a _____ pose for a moment.

8. The teacher was a _____ elderly man with snow-white hair.

9. On most of his journeys the boy was _____ until someone took pity on him and gave him some food.

10. The teacher's house was a _____ to the boy.

Short Answer: Write one or two complete sentences to answer each of the following questions.

1. What does the mother mean when she says "It's a sign; I believe in signs"?

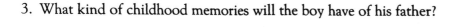

2. What eventually killed Sounder?

3. What kind of childhood memories will the boy have of his father?

Name: _____ Date: _____

Final Test
Sounder

Interpretation: Even though the boy's family was not educated in book ways, they were very intelligent when nature (either outdoors or human) was concerned. Explain what these sayings meant.

1. "Animals don't like to move much when it's windy." (p. 6)

2. "Don't shine too bright, you'll make the creatures skittish." (p. 40)

Multiple Choice: Choose the one best answer to each of the following. Write the letter of the correct answer in the blank.

1. _____ The boy's father was imprisoned for   (a) only 6 weeks   (b) 3 months   (c) one year   (d) several years.

2. _____ The boy's mother would tell stories from   (a) the newspaper   (b) Grimm's Fairy Tales   (c) the Bible   (d) Aesop.

3. _____ The boy's father had been injured in prison from   (a) a beating   (b) an avalanche in a mine   (c) a truck accident   (d) a tornado.

4. _____ When the father returned home at the end, Sounder   (a) wouldn't even come to him at first   (b) acted like a young dog again   (c) was too old to see him   (d) growled at him.

5. _____ The boy's father died   (a) in the woods   (b) back in prison   (c) the first night home   (d) from a gunshot wound.

6. _____ The first book that the boy found was written by   (a) Shakespeare   (b) Montaigne   (c) Dickens   (d) Alcott.

7. _____ Sounder was known for his   (a) intelligence   (b) kind eyes   (c) deep bark and howl   (d) two white paws.

8. _____ After his dog had been shot, the boy found   (a) a gun on the side of the house   (b) the deputy's identification card   (c) part of Sounder's ear   (d) a litter of puppies.

9. _____ The boy's mother told the boy that the dog crawled off into the woods to get healed by   (a) the old man in the swamp   (b) oakleaf acid   (c) sumac branches   (d) poison ivy.

10. _____ The boy's mother always told the boy that   (a) his learning was the most important thing   (b) he should never forget his family   (c) field work was good work   (d) he should respect his elders.

Answer Key

Sounder *(Worksheet, Chapters 1–4)*

Sequencing   ### Character Identification

3, 2, 4, 6, 5, 1, 7
1. a	4. c	7. a	10. c	13. b
2. b	5. a	8. b	11. a	14. c
3. c	6. c	9. c	12. b	15. a

Sounder *(Worksheet, Chapters 5–8)*

Vocabulary

1. sneer	4. compulsion	7. defiant	10. sanctuary
2. drought	5. cistern	8. lean	
3. withered	6. mellow	9. famished	

Short Answer (Answer may vary.)

1. The boy's mother believed that when the boy found the teacher it was God's way of leading her son to education. This was the "sign" of which she spoke, and she was very religious and believed strongly in these signs.

2. Sounder was injured horribly by the gunshot wound, but what finally killed him was the death of his master, the boy's father. He lost the will to live.

3. The boy says that the nights hunting in the woods with his father and Sounder will be memorable.

Final Test

Interpretation (Answers may vary.)

1. The father tells the boy that animals in the woods won't come out in windy weather because they can't pick up the scent of a dog (or other animal) that might attack them. So, when it's windy, they don't move around as much as usual.

2. This line is said to the moon. When the moon is full and shines brightly, all nature acts a little differently. Even Sounder would howl to the moon in a different way.

Multiple Choice

1. d	3. b	5. a	7. c	9. b
2. c	4. b	6. b	8. c	10. a

Extension Activities

Sounder

Discussion

CHAPTER 1
1. Why do you think the father went out at night without Sounder?
2. Why does the mother's humming bother the boy so much?

CHAPTER 2
1. Do you think Sounder is healing himself or dying?
2. How were the deputies unduly rude and rough?

CHAPTER 3
1. The boy thought, "People would be very mean to his mother today." Explain what he meant.

CHAPTER 4
1. How is "wood quiet" different from "cabin quiet"? Do you agree?
2. How did the deputy sheriff degrade the boy?
3. What causes people to be prejudiced?
4. Why doesn't the father want the boy to come visit anymore?

CHAPTER 5
1. How has Sounder changed?

CHAPTER 6
1. Even if the boy is about 12 years of age, why would he know that he "had lived a long, long time"? What experiences age children faster than they should?
2. What encourages the boy through his journeys?

CHAPTER 7
1. At their first meeting, what things surprised the boy about the teacher?
2. In what ways is the teacher the kindest person the boy has met on his journeys?

CHAPTER 8
1. Why did the mother agree to let him go stay with the teacher?
2. What is the one thing that caused Sounder to start barking again? Why do you think this is so?
3. How is Sounder smarter than the people?
4. At the end, how does the boy know Sounder will soon die?

General Discussion

1. Why didn't the author give any names to the people in the story?
2. What does the dog Sounder symbolize?
3. What does prejudice teach a child?
4. Although the date of this story is never given, how have times changed since the time of the story?

(continued)

Sounder (continued)

Reading

1. A good, short companion book to *Sounder* is *The Friendship* by Mildred D. Taylor. It tells of prejudice in the South during the 1930's and the friendship between a black man and a white man that is sorely tested.

2. A more difficult and longer book that is also centered on the prejudice and injustice in the South during the 1930's is *To Kill a Mockingbird* by Harper Lee. Mature readers would find this book engrossing.

Writing

1. Have students read the Author's Note about whose story this really is. Then, as the boy, have them write their own addendum to the story. Did they continue schooling? Move away from their own home?

2. The father never says much about what happened to him in prison. If he could have written, what would have been his story?

Research

Have students study examples from history, such as the following, where deep prejudice determined who would be treated fairly and who would not.

- Nazi Germany
- South Africa
- Slavery in the U.S.
- The genocide movement against Native Americans
- The Spanish Inquisition

Video

The movie *Sounder* is a beautifully made film that is available for commercial rental or purchase. Filmed in 1972, it is rated G and runs 105 minutes. After students have read the book and viewed the film, have them talk about how the film differs from the book.

Art

Have students draw pictures of what Sounder would have looked like according to his description in Chapter 1. Viewing books about different breeds of dogs will help students.

Drama

In Chapter 7 the boy meets the teacher. At the end of the chapter the boy begins his story of his life. Write this out and have students read it in play format.

SPECIAL
CHALLENGES

The Crossing

by Gary Paulsen

Synopsis

Manny Bustos has known only one thing in his first 14 years of life—the streets of Juárez, Mexico. He has learned to survive by stealing, begging, and lying, but his dream is to cross over into the United States and have a better life. Sergeant Robert Locke also has dreams, but only of a terrifying nature. He drinks to forget . . . friends who have died, war, the army. He drinks to become "brain dead." In an alley in Juárez the two meet and nothing is the same again.

Vocabulary

CHAPTER 1
1. wiry
2. scorching

CHAPTER 2
1. slippage
2. sterile
3. prescribed
4. demerits

CHAPTER 3
1. eddies
2. diverted
3. snare
4. litany
5. vicious

CHAPTER 4
1. garish
2. obliterating
3. hamlet
4. devious
5. bouncer
6. barrios

CHAPTER 5
1. culvert
1. tactics
3. resolve
4. majority
5. defy
6. cunning
7. guttural

CHAPTER 6
1. careened
2. crowing
3. hovered
4. khaki
5. ultimate
6. absolute

CHAPTER 7
1. produce (n)
2. caution

CHAPTER 8
1. brittle
2. interdict
3. proclamation
4. exotic
5. mango
6. numbness

CHAPTER 9
1. matador
2. flatter
3. massive
4. solemn

CHAPTER 10
1. picador
2. rigid
3. lance

CHAPTER 11
1. rage

CHAPTER 12
1. feinted

Spanish Words to Know

frijoles = beans
salsa = sauce
sí = yes
turistas = tourists
Dios = God
Madre de Dios = Mother of God
Mestizo = half-breed
macho = manly
gringos = white people
serapes = shawls
sombrero = hat
bandidos = outlaws
plaza de toros = bullring plaza
banderillas = barbed sticks used on bulls
Hola = Hello
Norte Americano = North American

Name: _____   Date: _____

The Crossing—Chapters 1–6

Character Description: Manny and the sergeant live completely different lives. Fill in the spaces with appropriate descriptions taken from your knowledge of the book.

	SLEEPING ARRANGEMENT	AGE	PHYSICAL APPEARANCE	BACKGROUND	FEARS
MANNY					
SERGEANT LOCKE					

Multiple Choice: Choose the one best answer to each of the following. Write the letter of that choice in the blank.

1. _____ This novel takes place in   (a) Mexico City   (b) California   (c) Albuquerque, New Mexico   (d) Juárez, Mexico.

2. _____ Manny is easy to spot on the streets because   (a) of his bright green jacket   (b) of the red hat he always wears   (c) of his red hair   (d) of his height.

3. _____ Sergeant Locke's favorite "hangout" was   (a) a church   (b) Riki Tiki Tavi   (c) Club Congo Tiki   (d) Club Paradise.

4. _____ The first time they met, what did *not* happen?   (a) Manny tried to rob the sergeant.   (b) The sergeant gave Manny $20.   (c) The sergeant almost took Manny over the bridge.   (d) They met in an alley.

5. _____ In Manny's world, "coyotes" are   (a) people who take Mexicans across the border for money   (b) American GI's   (c) girls living with the nuns   (d) people who watch the borders for illegal crossings.

6. _____ The turistas would   (a) ignore the young boys at the bridge   (b) take children across the bridge on Sundays   (c) throw money to the young boys   (d) only shop and never eat in Juárez.

7. _____ The one thing that is constant in Manny's life is   (a) his mother   (b) his brother   (c) Maria's food   (d) hunger.

8. _____ Worse than the coyotes are the   (a) Americans   (b) evil street men   (c) border patrolmen   (d) priests.

9. _____ The best adjective for Manny would be   (a) cheerful   (b) lazy   (c) resourceful   (d) cruel.

10. _____ Manny learned English   (a) in order to beg from the Americans   (b) from the nuns at the convent   (c) from Sergeant Locke   (d) in order to go to school.

Name: _____ Date: _____

The Crossing—Chapters 7–12

Vocabulary: Match up the vocabulary and special references found in the book. Write the letter of the reference in the correct blank.

1. _____ Pancho Villa
2. _____ numbness
3. _____ banderilla
4. _____ plaza de toros
5. _____ Hola
6. _____ matador
7. _____ turistas
8. _____ Norte Americano
9. _____ bouncer
10. _____ massive

(a) Person who stopped Manny from going into the club

(b) What Robert is, according to Manny

(c) Bullfighter

(d) Famous Mexican bandit

(e) What the sergeant hopes for when "brain dead"

(f) Item used on bulls during bullfights

(g) Spanish greeting

(h) Size of bull

(i) The bullfight ring

(j) tourists

Sequencing: Number from 1 to 6 in the correct order in which these events happened in the book.

_____ Manny goes to his first bullfight.

_____ Sergeant Locke is killed.

_____ Locke gives his wallet to Manny.

_____ Manny has a full breakfast, probably his first.

_____ Manny gives the bullfight poster to the sergeant.

_____ Manny first tries to pickpocket Sergeant Locke.

Short Essay: Write complete sentences to answer each of the following questions.

1. How do you think Manny's life will be different now?

2. If Manny had never met the sergeant, what would have been the probable outcome of Manny's life? (Give at least two different options.)

Final Test
The Crossing

Multiple Response: Choose as many answers as are needed in order to correctly complete the following statements. This means you may choose only one letter, or as many as all four. Write the letter(s) of your choice(s) in the blank.

1. _____ Sergeant Locke drank to (a) become more adventurous (b) be like the other men (c) forget bad memories (d) become "brain dead."

2. _____ Manny's life was characterized by (a) poverty (b) a very close family (c) loneliness (d) day-to-day survival techniques.

3. _____ The only people who ever showed kindness to Manny were (a) the sergeant (b) Maria (c) Pancho (d) the village priest.

4. _____ Because of the sergeant, some of Manny's "firsts" were (a) his first fishing trip (b) his first restaurant meal (c) his first bullfight (d) his first pair of shoes.

5. _____ At the very end (a) the street men gang up on Sergeant Locke (b) Manny tells the sergeant the truth about his crossing (c) Sergeant Locke gives his wallet to Manny before dying (d) Sergeant Locke is stabbed.

Spanish Vocabulary: Use the Spanish words listed below to fill in the blanks correctly.

salsa	Mestizo	macho	frijoles	plaza de toros
turistas	Norte Americano	sí	banderillas	

To Manny, his life revolved around the _____ and how much money they would throw. Even though Pancho called Manny a _____ , he would fight for the money along with the others. Manny didn't really care about being _____ ; he just wanted to survive.

For food, Manny would sometimes beg a tortilla and some _____ from Maria. With _____ the beans were delicious.

When Manny met the sergeant he said to himself, " _____ , this is one _____ who may give me some money." But the sergeant gave Manny more than money. The sergeant took him to the _____ where he saw the picadors place the _____ in the bulls' necks during the fight. That day was a day like no other for Manny, one full of food and excitement.

Essay: Write a complete paragraph to answer the following:

Survival is a theme of *The Crossing*. Compare and contrast the survival techniques of Manny and the sergeant. Use examples from the book to support your ideas.

Answer Key

The Crossing *(Worksheet, Chapters 1–6)*

Character Description (Answers will vary.)

	SLEEPING ARRANGEMENT	AGE	PHYSICAL APPEARANCE	BACKGROUND	FEARS
MANNY	Sleeps underneath a cardboard box. Lives on the streets, trying to be as inconspicuous as possible.	Probably 14.	Red hair, small for his age, thin from starvation.	Was left at a church when he was a baby, but soon ended up on the streets.	That he will be taken by street men; beaten up by older boys.
SERGEANT LOCKE	Army regulation barracks.	18 yrs. in the army, probably about 36–38.	Graying hair, blue eyes, very neat army uniform, one scar on face.	Grew up in Kansas; has memories of many forts and wars in Vietnam and El Salvador.	That his old friends will haunt him; that he won't be able to forget with drinking.

Multiple Choice

1. d	6. c
2. c	7. d
3. c	8. b
4. b	9. c
5. a	10. a

The Crossing *(Worksheet, Chapters 7–12)*

Vocabulary

1. d	6. c
2. e	7. j
3. f	8. b
4. i	9. a
5. g	10. h

Sequencing

4, 6, 5, 2, 3, 1

(continued)

Short Essay (Answers will vary.)

1. He may have the chance to cross over into the U.S. With money, at least he will not starve for a while, but it remains doubtful where he would get work, housing, or even education.

2. He said himself that he could not survive much longer. He was smaller than the other boys and the street men were always waiting to grab him and sell him. Death from starvation was also another close reality.

Final Test

Multiple Response

1. c, d
2. a, c, d
3. a, b
4. b, c
5. a, b, c, d

Spanish Vocabulary

(Given in the order that the words should be placed in the blanks.)

turistas	frijoles	Norte Americano
Mestizo	salsa	plaza de toros
macho	Sí	banderillas

Essay (Answers will vary.)

Both the sergeant and Manny take each day at a time. However, Sergeant Locke no longer has to worry about basic survival techniques as Manny does because his basic needs are met. But the sergeant does use mental survival techniques to get him through each day. Drinking is his best escape to make him "brain dead." He also uses the "sergeant" image in order to ignore many of his problems. For Manny, each day is a trick to stay alive. He knows the survival techniques of the street: stealing, begging, being ever watchful. He is most industrious, knowing where to be at the right time.

Extension Activities

The Crossing

Discussion

CHAPTER 1

1. What kind of life does Manny have?
2. What does Manny expect to get when he crosses into the U.S.? Is this a realistic view?

CHAPTER 2

1. Why does the sergeant want to be "brain dead"?
2. Instead of alcohol, what would be some other solutions to his depression?

CHAPTER 3

1. Why is it impossible for Manny to get money off the bridge?
2. What is the futility of Manny's life?

CHAPTER 4

1. What memories of Vietnam does the sergeant have?
2. How is the sergeant different from most of the men in the bar?

CHAPTER 5

1. Who are the "coyotes"?
2. Why is nighttime a dangerous time for Manny?

CHAPTER 6

1. Why wasn't Manny able to cross this night?
2. What surprised Manny about the sergeant?

CHAPTER 7

1. Who was Pancho Villa and why does Manny idolize him?

CHAPTER 8

1. Why do you think the sergeant bought breakfast for Manny?
2. Symbolically, what do you think it meant when the sergeant said, "The boy has no cover"?

CHAPTER 9

1. Why do you think Robert wanted to see a bullfight?
2. Was the bullfight a different experience for Manny than it was for Robert? Explain.

CHAPTER 10

1. What was Robert talking about when he said, "It's all a game"?

CHAPTER 11

1. Why was it getting almost impossible for Manny to survive?
2. Why didn't Manny ever tell the truth?

CHAPTER 12

1. What does Manny intend to do immediately after the sergeant's death?
2. How will the sergeant's death affect Manny?

Reading

1. Young adult novels about modern-day Hispanics are not as abundant as one would wish. However, here are some excellent choices for young people:

The Honorable Prison by Becerra de Jenkins
Viva, Chicano by Frank Bonham

(continued)

Corky and the Brothers Cool by P. J. Petersen
The Maldonado Miracle by Theodore Taylor

2. Gary Paulsen has become one of the frontrunners of young adult literature in the past decade. His books often deal with survival from the male viewpoint and offer some quality reading. The following are some of his best books available for teens:

* *Hatchet*	*The Voyage of the Frog*	*Canyons*
Dogsong	*The Winter Room*	*Dancing Carl*
Sentries	*Tracker*	*The Foxman*

* covered in this volume

Writing

Have students write an Afterword to the story. Place the time either a month later, a year later, or several years later. Before writing, students should consider these questions:

• Did Manny ever make it over the border?

• What if border patrolmen had caught Manny with the sergeant's wallet . . . and then found the sergeant dead?

• What obstacles would Manny have encountered if he actually made it across to the U.S.?

Research

1. Have students research some of the information and statistics related to illegal and legal crossings from Mexico to the United States. Almanacs are a good source of statistics of immigration numbers.

2. Francisco "Pancho" Villa (1877?–1923) is a colorful person for students to research. He was a revolutionary leader who was assassinated. Biographies and almost any encyclopedia will provide information about him.

3. There are hundreds of Spanish words (such as *cafeteria, patio, rodeo*) that are now an integral part of American speech. Have a group of students do a survey, asking people how many Spanish words they know. Have the group compile the results and report to the class.

Art

Have students draw a map of Mexico, coloring in the states and labeling major cities and states.

Hatchet

by Gary Paulsen

Synopsis

While Brian is flying over the Canadian wilderness to visit his father, his pilot has a heart attack and dies. Brian miraculously survives the crash landing, only to have his survival skills tested constantly for the next two months. Brian learns to respect and fit in with the environment and succeeds, in part, because of a small hatchet.

Vocabulary

CHAPTER 1
1. altitude
2. stewed
3. horizon
4. hokey
5. audible
6. contracted

CHAPTER 2
1. turbulence
2. procedures
3. cowling
4. indicate
5. altimeter
6. depress

CHAPTER 3
1. wallow

CHAPTER 4
1. moderately
2. hummocks

CHAPTER 5
1. murky
2. amphibious
3. asset

CHAPTER 6
1. lean-to
2. diminish
3. glacier
4. pulverized
5. interlaced

CHAPTER 7
1. seepage

CHAPTER 8
NONE

CHAPTER 9
1. haunches
2. exasperation
3. Cro-Magnon

CHAPTER 10
1. eddied
2. dormant

CHAPTER 11
1. comprised

CHAPTER 12
1. persistent
2. abruptly

CHAPTER 13
1. virtual
2. refracts

CHAPTER 14
1. sulfurous

CHAPTER 15
1. stabilize

CHAPTER 16
1. debated

CHAPTER 17
1. crosspieces
2. stymied
3. vertical
4. fuselage

CHAPTER 18
1. substantial

CHAPTER 19
NONE

EPILOGUE
1. furor
2. predators

Hatchet—Chapters 1–7

Vocabulary: Fill in the blanks with appropriate words taken from the vocabulary lists for Chapters 1–7.

1. Like pop without fizz, he held the bag up and let the _____ drip into his mouth.

2. Brian figured the rescuers would come in an _____ plane that could land on water.

3. When he pulled back on the wheel the plane slowed dramatically and just seemed to _____ in the air.

4. Brian put on the pilot's headset and reached to _____ the switch that turned it on.

5. The _____ was the device that told him his height above ground.

6. Other dials seemed to _____ what the wings were doing.

7. During the heart attack the pilot's legs _____ up into the seat.

8. The plane clawed for _____ during take-off.

9. Using branches, Brian _____ a wall across the opening of the front rock.

10. Brian reminded himself that he was his own best _____ .

11. The country around the lake was _____ hilly.

12. He repeated the radio calls many times at ten-minute _____ .

13. Some of the rock had been scooped out and then _____ by glacial action into a small sand beach.

14. After the pilot died, the plane hit a bit of _____ , and Brian realized he would have to take control.

15. Ordinarily Brian would have said that it was too _____ to wear a hatchet on his belt.

Trivia Busters: Fill in the blanks with the correct details from the book.

1. To whom did the author dedicate this book?

_____

2. What kind of plane was Brian flying?

_____

3. At the beginning of the book, Brian was on his way to see his _____ .

4. The hatchet was a gift from his _____ .

Hatchet—Chapters 8-Epilogue

Vocabulary: Fill in the blanks with appropriate words taken from the vocabulary lists for Chapters 8-Epilogue.

1. Without feathers to _____ it, his arrow would turn and miss the mark.

2. Brian suddenly realized that the _____ whine in the distance was a search plane.

3. The hunger which had been _____ until now awoke with a vengeance when he held the egg.

4. Brian thought that even a _____ man would have had a fire lit by now.

5. He moved to the top of the rock ridge that _____ the bluff.

6. Although game was plentiful in the fall, in the winter the _____ sweep through and wipe it out.

7. The _____ , the plane's body toward the tail, was out of the water.

8. He only had two arrows, so Brian _____ about shooting again.

9. The thick, _____ odor from the skunk filled the room.

10. As he sat in the water, he was surrounded by a _____ cloud of small fish.

11. The sound moved away _____ as the plane turned to the south.

12. He had forgotten that water _____ and bends light.

13. Keeping the branches for the raft together without _____ and nails seemed impossible.

14. Brian was interviewed for several networks but the _____ died down soon.

15. At first, Brian was _____ about building the raft. Then, the answer came to him.

Trivia Busters: Fill in the blanks with the correct details from the book.

1. Brian solved the mosquito problem by _____

   _____ .

2. The train sound that Brian heard was really a _____

   _____ .

3. The first thing that Brian offered to the rescue pilot was _____ .

Final Test
Hatchet

Sequencing: Number from 1 to 10 in the order in which these events happened in the book.

_____ Brian offered the rescue pilot some food.

_____ Brian makes a bow and arrow.

_____ Brian gets interviewed on TV.

_____ Brian finds turtle eggs.

_____ Brian builds a fire.

_____ Brian dives for the hatchet.

_____ Brian flies the plane.

_____ Brian turns on the transmitter.

_____ Brian has a completely insane day.

_____ Brian learns his mother's secret.

True/False: Write *true* or *false* for each of the following statements.

1. _____ Brian's parents had been divorced for two years.

2. _____ The pilot told Brian how to land the plane.

3. _____ Brian had taken a course on wilderness survival.

4. _____ The bear chased Brian to the rocky bluff area of the lake.

5. _____ Brian was attacked by both a skunk and porcupine.

6. _____ Brian cooked the turtle eggs in an old can he found by the lake.

7. _____ Brian used his watch crystal to make the fire.

8. _____ After the moose attacked him, he realized a tornado was coming.

9. _____ Brian flew the plane for over an hour after the pilot died.

10. _____ The tornado repositioned the tail of the plane up out of the lake.

Short Essay: Answer the following question in a complete paragraph.

What is the meaning of the book's title, *Hatchet*?

Answer Key

Hatchet (*Worksheet, Chapters 1–7*)

Vocabulary

1. seepage	4. depress	7. contracted	10. asset	13. pulverized
2. amphibious	5. altimeter	8. altitude	11. moderately	14. turbulence
3. wallow	6. indicate	9. interlaced	12. intervals	15. hokey

Trivia Busters

1. The students of Hershey Middle School
2. Cessna 406 or Bush Plane
3. father
4. mother

Hatchet (*Worksheet, Chapters 8–Epilogue*)

Vocabulary

1. stabilize	4. Cro-Magnon	7. fuselage	10. virtual	13. crosspieces
2. persistent	5. comprised	8. debated	11. abruptly	14. furor
3. dormant	6. predators	9. sulfurous	12. refracts	15. stymied

Trivia Busters

1. building a fire (The flames and the smoke kept them away.)
2. tornado
3. some food

Final Test

Sequencing

9, 5, 10, 3, 4, 7, 2, 8, 6, 1

True/False

1. false	4. false	7. false	10. true
2. false	5. true	8. true	
3. false	6. false	9. true	

Short Essay (Answers may vary.)

Because of a small hatchet, which Brian had made fun of at first, he actually survived in the wilderness. On a literal level, the hatchet was a tool and a weapon. On a symbolic level the hatchet represented courage in the midst of uncertainty. To Brian, his confidence grew because of this small hatchet and his ability to use it to meet many demands.

Extension Activities

Hatchet

Discussion

CHAPTER 1

1. What does Brian spend his time thinking about during the flight?
2. How did Brian get the hatchet? Where is it?

CHAPTER 2

1. Where does Brian want to land? Why?
2. How long has Brian been flying? How far do you think he has traveled?
3. What does the countryside look like?

CHAPTER 3

1. What causes the explosion?

CHAPTER 4

1. What kinds of injuries does Brian have?

CHAPTER 5

1. What materials and resources does Brian have?
2. What does Brian realize about the plane's course?

CHAPTER 6

1. Describe Brian's new home.
2. How "easy" was it to find food?

CHAPTER 7

1. What does Brian realize after seeing the bear?
2. What is the secret Brian is keeping?

CHAPTER 8

1. How did Brian learn to make sparks?
2. What important rule of survival did Brian learn?

CHAPTER 9

1. What process did Brian use to start a fire?

CHAPTER 10

1. What are the advantages of having a fire? What are the disadvantages?
2. How has Brian's sleeping pattern changed? Why?

CHAPTER 11

1. Why did Brian fish before?
2. What helps his depression?
3. In what way does Brian "see" differently now?

CHAPTER 12

1. In what ways was it difficult to catch a fish?
2. How does the plane's visit change Brian's attitude?

CHAPTER 13

1. What two truths does Brian learn?
2. How does he finally catch a fish?
3. How did Brian react to the wolves?

CHAPTER 14

1. How does Brian save for the future?
2. How long has Brian been living by the lakes?

CHAPTER 15

1. In what way is Brian now a better hunter?

CHAPTER 16

1. What two events happened on the "insane day"?
2. How did part of the plane become visible?

(continued)

87

CHAPTER 17

1. How has Brian used his windbreaker to survive during this wilderness experience?

CHAPTER 18

1. Why was Brian reluctant to get inside the plane?

2. What made the hatchet so important that Brian was willing to risk his life for it?

CHAPTER 19

1. How did the rifle make Brian feel different?

2. How did the pilot locate Brian?

EPILOGUE

1. Could Brian have survived a winter there alone at the lake? Why or why not?

2. Why does Brian keep the secret?

3. How has Brian changed?

Reading

1. Students who enjoyed this book will enjoy reading Paulsen's sequel to it, *The River*. Other books by Gary Paulsen are:

   Dancing Carl   *The Winter Room*
   Dogsong   *The Boy Who Owned the School*
   Sentries   *The Voyage of the Frog*
   Tracker   * *The Crossing*
   The Cookcamp

   * covered in this volume

2. Other books about survival in nature are:

   The Elephant Tree by Harriet Luger
   The Voyage of the Frog by Gary Paulsen
   ** *Snow Bound* by Harry Mazer
   * *Julie of the Wolves* by Jean Craighead George
   Deathwatch by Robb White
   * *Cave Under the City* by Harry Mazer

   * covered in this volume
   ** covered in Volume II of this series

Writing

1. Write a short essay discussing the changes in Brian. Predict what he would be like as an adult—what career he would select, his relationships, his outlook on modern living.

2. In the Epilogue, the author says that Brian was interviewed by several networks. Imagine yourself to be a major network news anchor who interviews Brian. What questions would you ask? How do you think Brian would respond? What would your audience want to know?

(continued)

Research

Students who want more information on subjects covered in this book could research the following:

(a) Search and rescue teams around the country as well as in your own community.

(b) True wilderness stories chronicled in books or newspapers.

(c) Federal Aviation Association procedures to locate downed aircraft.

(d) Outward Bound programs or wilderness survival programs available around the country or in your area.

(e) Human and other predators' places in the ecological balance of animals and nature.

Art

Illustrate a scene for each chapter from the book for a *Newsweek* story on Brian Robeson's wilderness survival.

Video

As part of the Wonderworks series, PBS produced "A Cry in the Wild" in the fall of 1991. The special is based directly on Paulsen's *Hatchet*.

Julie of the Wolves

by Jean Craighead George

Synopsis

She is 13 years old. Miyax—daughter of the hunter Kapugen, named Julie at the B.I.A. (Bureau of Indian Affairs) school in Barrow, Alaska, and child bride of the detestable Daniel—is now a runaway in the Arctic wilderness. She knows from her father's teachings that in order for her to survive, she will have to become "one" among the pack of wolves she has been watching for days. Throughout this period of aloneness Miyax learns to think about her life and what she truly wants.

Vocabulary

PART 1

Pages 5–25
1. harpoon
2. predicament
3. barren
4. immensity
5. cosmos
6. regal
7. caribou
8. kayak
9. tundra
10. brittle
11. monotony
12. lemming
13. frenzy
14. phenomenon
15. prey
16. vitality
17. dominance
18. semaphore
19. undulating
20. roughhousing

Pages 25–37
1. soliciting
2. winced
3. heave
4. carrion
5. laboriously
6. regurgitated
7. deference
8. torso

Pages 37–61
1. induce
2. hamper
3. hostile
4. knoll
5. warily
6. nomadic
7. sedge
8. plummeting
9. acute
10. demonic
11. bunting
12. owlet
13. dispute
14. apogee
15. quell
16. incorrigible
17. discern
18. immobile
19. improvisation
20. crescendo
21. reprimand

Pages 61–70
1. predator

PART II

Pages 75–98
1. taut
2. derisively
3. prosperous
4. remote
5. macadam

Pages 98–104
NONE

PART III

Pages 109–122
1. bestial
2. abeyance
3. lair
4. cumbersome
5. disquieting
6. contorted
7. cowed

Pages 122–138
1. simplicity
2. bounty
3. plumage
4. ravenously

Pages 138–162
1. meandering
2. artifacts
3. grandeur
4. rodents
5. treacherous
6. advent
7. enamored

Pages 163–170
1. resonant

Julie of the Wolves—**Part I (Pages 5–70)**

Character Identification: Write the character's letter in the blank beside each description of that character. You may use a letter more than once.

(a) Amaroq   (c) Daniel   (e) Kapugen   (g) Jello

(b) Amy   (d) Julie (Miyax)   (f) Silver   (h) Kapu

1. _____ Lived in San Francisco.
2. _____ Of the puppies, he seemed to be the little leader.
3. _____ Male wolf, but "low man on the totem pole."
4. _____ Undisputed leader of the wolf pack.
5. _____ Julie's pen pal.
6. _____ Runaway 13-year-old wife.
7. _____ Miyax's father.
8. _____ Mother of wolf pups.
9. _____ Julie's "husband."
10. _____ Known as a great Eskimo hunter.
11. _____ The boldest of the black puppies.
12. _____ Stays on hands and knees in order to be accepted by wolves.

Short Answer: Write the answer to each of the following questions in complete sentences.

1. What tools of survival does Miyax possess?

2. How did Miyax become one of the wolf pack?

3. What are at least two myths about wolves that are incorrect?

4. Who is Kapugen and why is he such an influence on Julie at this point in her life?

Julie of the Wolves—Parts II & III (Pages 75–170)

Multiple Choice: Choose the one best answer to complete the statement correctly. Write the letter of that choice in the blank.

1. _____ After Miyax's mother died   (a) Miyax went to live in San Francisco   (b) her father sent Miyax to marry Daniel   (c) Miyax lived with her father at the seal camp   (d) Miyax disappeared into the Arctic for about two months.

2. _____ Julie "met" Amy   (a) at a cultural exchange conference   (b) through Amy's father   (c) at her new school   (d) in San Francisco.

3. _____ Julie's marriage agreement had been signed by   (a) Kapugen and his wife   (b) Kapugen and Martha   (c) Kapugen and Naka   (d) Daniel and Julie.

4. _____ After arriving in Barrow to meet Daniel   (a) Julie was married the very next day   (b) Julie and Daniel waited a month before marrying   (c) Julie and Daniel decided not to get married   (d) Julie wanted to wait until she was 16 before marrying.

5. _____ After her marriage, Julie's main duty was to   (a) clean out the cabins for the tourists   (b) take tourists on fishing trips   (c) please Daniel   (d) sew parkas for tourists.

6. _____ The biggest fault with Naka was that he   (a) drank too much and was then violent   (b) was too kind to the tourists   (c) gave Daniel everything he wanted   (d) was too shy.

7. _____ Julie's best friend in Barrow was   (a) Naka   (b) Daniel   (c) Martha   (d) Pearl.

8. _____ At what point did Miyax decide never to go to San Francisco?   (a) The day Daniel attacked her.   (b) The day that Amaroq was killed.   (c) The day she found Tornait.   (d) The day she found Kapugen.

9. _____ Which of the wolves turned on Miyax?   (a) Amaroq   (b) Kapu   (c) Jello   (d) Silver

10. _____ Miyax's first human visitors in the wild were   (a) Kapugen and his new wife   (b) Amy and her father   (c) Uma and Atik   (d) Daniel and Naka.

11. _____ Tornait was   (a) a fox   (b) a golden plover   (c) Miyax's uncle   (d) a pilot from Point Hope.

12. _____ Amaroq was killed   (a) by hunters just having some fun   (b) by another leader of a different wolf pack   (c) by Miyax and her father   (d) by starvation.

13. _____ Atik told Miyax that he was trained by   (a) the university professors   (b) Daniel   (c) his grandfather   (d) the greatest hunter, Kapugen.

14. _____ Upon meeting her father again, Miyax was a little surprised that he had   (a) married again   (b) married a gussack   (c) married someone so old   (d) been living in the wild.

15. _____ To Miyax, her adopted father will always be   (a) Tornait   (b) Naka   (c) Kapugen   (d) Amaroq.

Name: _____   Date: _____

Final Test
Julie of the Wolves

True/False: Write *true* or *false* for each of the following statements.

1. _____ Miyax's father has married a non-Eskimo woman who is a teacher.

2. _____ Tornait was just one of the many birds that are frequently seen in the North.

3. _____ Miyax is surprised to find out she has a half-brother now.

4. _____ Miyax tells her father that she blames him for making her marry Daniel.

5. _____ Miyax's father now lives in the town of Barrow, Alaska.

Interpretation: In the space provided and on the back of this sheet, if necessary, complete the following:

1. On the final page, Miyax sings this song to the spirit of Amaroq:

> The seals are scarce and the whales are almost gone.
> The spirits of the animals are passing away.
> Amaroq, Amaroq, you are my adopted father.
> My feet dance because of you.
> My eyes see because of you.
> My mind thinks because of you. And it thinks, on this thundering
>   night,
> That the hour of the wolf and the Eskimo is over.

Interpret and explain what she means by these words.

2. As Miyax looked around her father's home, this is what she saw:

"This time she saw not just the furs and the kayak, but electric lamps, a radio-phonograph, cotton curtains and, through the door to the annex, the edge of an electric stove, a coffee pot, and china dishes. There were bookshelves and a framed picture on the wall of some American country garden."

Interpret the significance of what Miyax saw. What does all this indicate about Kapugen's life now?

Answer Key

Julie of the Wolves (*Worksheet, Part I*)

Character Identification

1. b
2. h
3. g
4. a
5. b
6. d
7. e
8. f
9. c
10. e
11. h
12. d

Short Answer (Answers may vary.)

1. Miyax possesses a knife, an ulo, wooden matches, and needles. With these "tools" she can build and make almost everything she needs.

2. She watched the wolf pack constantly to find out ways that would make her part of the pack. She would approach them only on hands and knees and would eventually engage in the same kind of play and respectful treatment that all the pups showed toward Amaroq.

3. *Myth:* Wolves will attack humans. *Truth:* Wolves almost never attack humans unless directly threatened.

   Myth: Wolves are cruel and mean. *Truth:* Wolves are very loving and protective.

   Myth: Wolves are solitary animals. *Truth:* Wolves belong to packs, taking care of their young and wounded.

4. Kapugen is Miyax's father. He is a great hunter in the Arctic and after Miyax's mother died, he took Miyax with him to the seal camp. There he taught her everything about hunting and survival. It is because of what Kapugen taught her that she was able to survive with the wolves.

Julie of the Wolves (*Worksheet, Parts II and III*)

Multiple Choice

1. c	3. c	5. d	7. d	9. c	11. b	13. d	15. d
2. b	4. a	6. a	8. b	10. c	12. a	14. b	

Final Test

True/False

1. true
2. false
3. false
4. false
5. false

Interpretation

1. Because of the wolves and Amaroq's acceptance of her, Julie is now alive. When she says "My feet dance because of you . . . ," she is saying everything she has now, life included, are because Amaroq helped her. But, as she thinks on these things, it saddens her because she knows things are changing. In order to survive she must put away the old ways of the Eskimo and join her father in his new life-style.

2. Just by this look around the room, Julie can figure out the following: her father is more modern now (electric lamps, stove, etc.). There are decorative touches that reflect his new wife's background and taste. By bringing her own books and photographs, she may also be extending Kapugen's world.

Extension Activities

Julie of the Wolves

Discussion

PART I

Pages 5–25

1. Which of the wolves has Miyax named and how did she decide on these names?
2. Why is it essential that Miyax communicate with the wolves?

Pages 25–37

1. How did Miyax finally get some food?
2. How is Miyax showing maturity and common sense in her situation?

Pages 37–61

1. What has happened to Jello in the pack?
2. Name all the ways that Miyax is helping herself to stay alive.

Pages 61–70

1. How has Amy been a source of strength and hope for Miyax?
2. At the end of this section, the wolves are gone. What does this mean for Julie?

PART II

Pages 75–98

1. Was Aunt Martha right to take Julie away from her father? Explain.
2. What is a "marriage of convenience"?

Pages 98–104

1. What prompted Julie to run away?
2. Why is she confident she can make it in the wilderness?

PART III

Pages 109–122

1. How did Miyax humiliate Jello?
2. How did Jello get revenge for this humiliation?
3. What finally happened to Jello and why?

Pages 122–138

1. Why does Miyax like the simplicity of her world?
2. Who are Tornait and Miyax and how did they help each other?

Pages 138–162

1. Why was the plane dangerous to Julie and the wolves?
2. How did Julie's view of life among people change at this time?
3. At the end of this section, what future awaits Miyax?

Pages 163–170

1. Describe the town of Kangik.
2. How was her meeting with her father disappointing to Miyax?
3. Why did she finally return to her father? Do you think this was a good decision? Why or why not?

(continued)

Julie of the Wolves (continued)

Reading

1. There are several good human vs. nature survival books for young adults. Here are some of them:

   Voyage of the Frog by Gary Paulsen (ocean survival)
   * *Hatchet* by Gary Paulsen (wilderness survival)
   Deathwatch by Robb White (desert survival)
   The Elephant Tree by Harriet Luger (desert survival)
   ** *Snow Bound* by Harry Mazer (wilderness survival)
   A Boat to Nowhere by Maureen Crane Wartski (ocean survival)
   Pursuit by Michael French (wilderness survival)

   * covered in this volume
   ** covered in Volume II of this series

2. *Julie of the Wolves* was the winner of the Newberry Medal for 1973. Students should read the other three honor books for that year and decide why this book won over the others. The Newberry Honor books for 1973 were: *Frog and Toad Together* by Arnold Lobel, *The Upstairs Room* by Johanna Reis, and *The Witches of Worm* by Zilpha Keatley Snyder.

3. Other books by Jean Craighead George that students might like to read are:

   The Cry of the Crow
   My Side of the Mountain
   The Summer of the Falcon

4. There are nonfiction books written about the life-style and customs of the Inuits. Recommend these to students who want more information about Miyax's tribe.

Writing

1. Amy's letters to Julie were very important to Julie. However, at one point in the book, Julie decides that she will never visit Amy in San Francisco and wants nothing to do with Amy's life-style. At the end of the book, Julie's ideas have again changed. Have students write the letter to Amy (in Julie's voice) that Julie might write after she has returned to her father.

2. Have students write an essay about survival in the Arctic wilderness, telling what they learned from the book. Students should be sure to write many of the methods that Miyax used to stay alive.

3. Have students brainstorm about potential survival situations in your particular geographic area and write these ideas on the board. For example, in the southern states, hurricane survival techniques might be discussed; in the Midwest, tornado and flooding survival techniques, etc. These brainstorming sessions could be turned into essays or even first-person accounts of survival techniques.

(continued)

Research

Julie of the Wolves is a naturalist's delight to read. Assign groups of students a certain animal to research and report back to the group. The following animals are all mentioned in the book.

black wolf	lemming
wolverine	caribou
jaeger	Arctic fox
snowshoe rabbit	ptarmigan
bunting	grizzly bear
golden plover	gray whales

Art

1. Have students create a diorama, painting the natural setting for the wolves and then making clay figures for the wolf pack that Miyax meets.

2. Have students create a picture notebook of the animals (or related animals) mentioned in the book. If students are artistic they may want to draw the animals, but clipping out pictures or tracing pictures could be acceptable for those who wish to do so. Students should label each picture with the following information:

   Animal's common name
   Animal's scientific name
   General characteristics
   General habitat
   Unusual traits
   Endangered species?

A Night Without Stars

by James Howe

Synopsis

Not only does 11-year-old Maria need heart surgery, she needs someone to explain what to expect from the surgical experience. Her questions are answered by Donald, an unlikely new friend the other kids call Monster Man. As an abused child, Donald was badly burned and permanently disfigured. But Donald's current problems are his negative attitude and isolation. Maria's and Donald's personalities balance each other, and together they earn a strong and enduring friendship.

Vocabulary

CHAPTER 1

1. brazenness
2. boisterous
3. maniacally
4. crimson
5. genetic
6. transplant
7. saint

CHAPTER 2

1. assumed
2. impassive
3. invalid
4. Madonna

CHAPTER 3

1. cardiac
2. pediatrics
3. disembodied
4. cherub
5. asymptomatic
6. manifesting
7. intern
8. recruits
9. mallets

CHAPTER 4

1. monitoring
2. distorted
3. transfixed
4. threshold
5. contemptuous
6. accolade
7. rosary

CHAPTER 5

1. pondering
2. complied
3. tentatively

CHAPTER 6

1. precautions
2. implanted
3. maneuvering
4. void

CHAPTER 7

1. cherished
2. contagious
3. avail
4. timid
5. meditation
6. macrame
7. inspired
8. mannequin
9. shrouded
10. cascaded
11. atrium
12. ventricle
13. partition

CHAPTER 8

1. affixed
2. retreated
3. fortress
4. averting
5. betrayed

CHAPTER 9

1. perilously
2. proclaimed
3. grotesque
4. dowry
5. diminish

CHAPTER 10

1. blanched
2. obligingly

CHAPTER 11

1. squeamishly
2. appalled
3. persevered
4. surreptitiously

Name: _____   Date: _____

A Night Without Stars—Chapters 1-6

Vocabulary: Fill in the blanks correctly with vocabulary words taken from the list below.

intern	assumed	rosary
distorted	Madonna	boisterous
cherub	asymptomatic	recruits
defect	crimson	genetic
threshold	precautions	accolade

1. Her mother cried and held her _____ beads in her hand while Maria was in surgery.

2. The girls were so impressed with Carlo that Maria called them new _____ for his fan club.

3. Until recently, Maria's heart problem was _____ but now she gets tired easily with exercise.

4. The hole in her heart was a _____ she had since birth.

5. The family always _____ that Father had had a hard day at work.

6. Joni blushed bright _____ when Tina teased her about Carlo.

7. Sometimes heart problems are _____ and therefore, are present at birth.

8. The doctor had features like a _____ , all round, pink, and innocent.

9. Sarah said she wasn't a doctor yet, just a very tired _____ .

10. Maria stood on the _____ of the playroom, seeing Donald for the first time.

11. "So neat" was Linda's highest _____ .

12. The IV and other tubes were used as _____ to monitor bodily functions.

13. In the moonlight her mother looked like a _____ in a painting.

14. Tina and Joni's laughter got so _____ that the jungle gym started to rock.

15. At first it seemed to Maria that Donald's face was a puffy, _____ monster mask.

Trivia Busters: Fill in the blanks with the correct details from the book.

1. Carlo wants to name their car _____ .

2. Maria's father works as a _____ .

3. The initials for Maria's heart condition are _____ .

4. One of the most important things for Maria to do after surgery is

_____ .

Name: _____ Date: _____

A Night Without Stars—Chapters 7–11

Vocabulary: Fill in the blanks correctly with vocabulary words taken from the list below.

atrium	avail	grotesque
contagious	betrayed	averting
surreptitiously	partition	appalled
blanched	ventricle	shrouded

1. The happy spirits Bonnie and Linda brought to the playground seemed

   _____ to the other children.

2. Maria _____ looked at the driver of the car out of the corner of her eye.

3. Donald was _____ his eyes so he wouldn't have to see the unasked questions in Joey's eyes.

4. The upper part of a human heart is called an _____ .

5. The lower part of the heart is called a _____ .

6. Donald drew a picture of an astronaut, then _____ the figure in heavy black lines.

7. Until Maria came, Lorna had made many different efforts with Donald, all to no

   _____ .

8. Donald's happiness _____ the usual look in his eyes.

9. The _____ picture in the advertisement did indeed resemble Donald.

10. Maria was _____ and fascinated, at the same time, that her friends had discussed what to wear to her funeral.

11. Donald's face had _____ to the color of white clay when he heard that Maria was going home.

12. Septum is the _____ or wall between the two ventricles of the heart.

Trivia Busters: Fill in the blanks with the correct details from the book.

1. Maria's favorite kind of ice cream was chocolate granola _____ .

2. Donald called his foster parents Mother and Father _____ .

3. The gift Carlo gave Maria in the hospital was a _____ .

4. The happy poem Donald wrote was about a _____ .

Name: _____ Date: _____

Final Test
A Night Without Stars

Character Identification: Write the character's name in the blank next to each description of that character. You may use a name more than once.

Maria Mr. Tirone Bonnie Donald
Carlo Joe Marlene Gotta Lotta
Mrs. Tirone Anna Lorna

1. _____ Talks to the children like people, not germs under a microscope.
2. _____ Got hit by a car and broke her leg.
3. _____ Knew a lot of jokes from staying in the hospital.
4. _____ Favorite book was *Charlotte's Web.*
5. _____ Told his mom he wanted to be a priest.
6. _____ Gave Maria a gray stuffed mouse.
7. _____ Asked if she needed to "widdle."
8. _____ Monster Man.
9. _____ Bought an old Chevy convertible.
10. _____ Gave a satin heart-shaped pillow.
11. _____ Nurse.
12. _____ Looked like John Travolta.
13. _____ Plans to take Spanish lessons.
14. _____ Wouldn't wear a wig.
15. _____ Mom died believing his lies.
16. _____ Kept the rosary close by.
17. _____ Explained to the Tirone family exactly what happened in surgery.
18. _____ Loved poetry.
19. _____ Looked like a Madonna in the moonlight.
20. _____ Was shivering with cold after the fire.
21. _____ Said the operation was really a transplant.
22. _____ Changed from a nice baby to a nonstop screaming machine.

Short Answer: Answer the following in one or two complete sentences.

Describe Mother and Father Schultz.

Answer Key

A Night Without Stars (*Worksheet, Chapters 1–6*)

Vocabulary

1. rosary
2. recruits
3. asymptomatic
4. defect
5. assumed
6. crimson
7. genetic
8. cherub
9. intern
10. threshold
11. accolade
12. precautions
13. Madonna
14. boisterous
15. distorted

Trivia Busters

1. Easy Goin'
2. subway conductor
3. VSD
4. cough

A Night Without Stars (*Worksheet, Chapters 7–11*)

Vocabulary

1. contagious
2. surreptitiously
3. averting
4. atrium
5. ventricle
6. shrouded
7. avail
8. betrayed
9. grotesque
10. appalled
11. blanched
12. partition

Trivia Busters

1. ripple
2. Schultz
3. gold car charm
4. frog

Final Test

Character Identification

1. Lorna
2. Bonnie
3. Donald
4. Donald
5. Mr. Tirone
6. Joey
7. Gotta Lotta
8. Donald
9. Carlo
10. Mr. Tirone
11. Gotta Lotta
12. Carlo
13. Lorna
14. Donald
15. Mr. Tirone
16. Mrs. Tirone
17. Maria
18. Donald
19. Mrs. Tirone
20. Donald
21. Marlene
22. Anna

Short Answer

They are Donald's current foster parents. They are strict and more like grandparents than parents. Donald likes them because they don't hit. They play Gin Rummy with Donald.

Extension Activities

A Night Without Stars

Discussion

CHAPTER 1

1. How well informed is Maria about her operation?
2. How do Maria's friends react to her news?

CHAPTER 2

1. How is Maria's father treated at home?
2. How does Maria's mother respond when Maria asks questions about the operation?
3. What is Maria afraid will happen?

CHAPTER 3

1. What is Maria's theory about doctors' shots?
2. What is Maria's reaction to the description of the Monster Man?

CHAPTER 4

1. What is Maria's first impression of Donald?
2. How would you describe Lorna's job?

CHAPTER 5

1. How is the book's title explained in this chapter?
2. What kind of childhood did Donald have?

CHAPTER 6

1. What were Maria's family members told to expect after the surgery?
2. How do you think hospitals today work with young patients and their families?

CHAPTER 7

1. What questions did Maria have after the operation?
2. How did Donald help Maria?

CHAPTER 8

1. How did Donald change his "tough-guy" image?

CHAPTER 9

1. How does Carlo explain God's role in Donald's life?
2. What two things are different about Donald's poem?

CHAPTER 10

1. What promise did Carlo make?

CHAPTER 11

1. How would you explain the poem in this chapter?

Reading

1. James Howe has written many diverse books. Students who enjoyed this book may enjoy reading these books by the same author.

The Sebastian Barth Mysteries

    Eat Your Poison, Dear
    What Eric Knew
    Stage Fright

    Morgan's Zoo
    Scared Silly

The Bunnicula books

    Bunnicula: A Rabbit Tale of Mystery
      (written by James and Deborah Howe)
    The Celery Stalks at Midnight
    Howliday Inn
    Nighty-Nightmare
    The Fright Before Christmas

(continued)

2. Other young adult books that deal with the issue of child abuse are *The Lottery Rose* by Irene Hunt, *Mary Jane Harper Cried Last Night* by Joanna Lee and T. S. Cook, and *The Pinballs* by Betsy Byars. The latter is covered in this volume.

3. Another good young adult book about hospital experiences is *Izzy, Willy-Nilly* by Cynthia Voight. Because of a car accident, the young, popular cheerleader has to have her leg amputated. This book is covered in Volume III of this series.

Writing

1. Write a short story about a personal experience in the hospital.

2. Write an epilogue for this book. Do Maria and Donald remain friends? What ultimately happens to Donald?

3. Imagine you can make new policies and programs for the pediatric surgery ward of DeWitte Hospital. How would you structure the programs?

4. Write a poem about Maria and Donald's new friendship.

Research

Students interested in gaining further information about topics in this book could research:

(a) New hospital programs and policies regarding pediatric patients. (Interviews would be very informative.)

(b) Information regarding genetic heart defects such as VSD.

(c) Information on cardiopulmonary by-pass (the heart-lung machine). What does it do? How does it work? Who invented it?

(d) The Human Heart.

Art

Illustrate a real human heart. What did Maria's heart look like? How would you decorate your own heart to show the "real" you?

Video

The 1985 film *Mask* is the story of a teenage boy dealing with his disfiguring disease. It is rated PG-13, is 120 minutes long, and is available for commercial purchase or rental.

MYSTERIES

The Dollhouse Murders

by Betty Ren Wright

Synopsis

Thirteen-year-old Amy is frustrated by the constant demands for attention and care made by her mentally handicapped sister. So when Aunt Clare offers to have Amy come and stay with her at the old family house in the country, Amy is delighted. There, Amy discovers a beautiful dollhouse in the attic. It is an exact replica of the family house, including little dolls that represent her great-grandparents and her father and Aunt Clare as children. But there is more for Amy to discover when she realizes the dolls are trying to reveal the secret about the murders that happened in the house 30 years ago.

Vocabulary

CHAPTER 1
1. exceptional
2. sarcastic
3. resentment
4. impudent
5. plaintive

CHAPTER 2
1. facade
2. exquisitely
3. accurate
4. invalid

CHAPTER 3
1. hermit
2. isolated
3. collapsed

CHAPTER 4
1. abandoned

CHAPTER 5
1. impertinence

CHAPTER 6
1. blunt
2. unpredictable
3. vividly

CHAPTER 7
1. taut
2. obituaries
3. reference
4. prominent

CHAPTER 8
1. remote
2. appraiser

CHAPTER 9
1. overreacted

CHAPTER 10
1. grimace
2. sidetracked

CHAPTER 11
NONE

CHAPTER 12
1. giddy
2. midst

CHAPTER 13
1. accustomed
2. reproof
3. discreetly

CHAPTER 14
1. lingered

CHAPTER 15
1. insensitive

CHAPTER 16
1. fiancé
2. confided

CHAPTER 17
1. subdued
2. imperceptibly

CHAPTER 18
1. binding

CHAPTER 19
1. serenity

Name: _____   Date: _____

The Dollhouse Murders—Chapters 1-9

Vocabulary: Fill in the blanks with appropriate words taken from the vocabulary lists for Chapters 1–9.

1. The old house was in an area _____ from other people and houses.

2. Lately it seemed that _____ for her sister was always boiling under the surface.

3. Aunt Clare seemed so happy and friendly one minute, and touchy and _____ the next.

4. Amy's grandparents were considered to be a _____ couple in the town of Claiborne.

5. Uncle James lived like a _____ in the old house, using only two rooms and rarely leaving.

6. Louann attended a school for _____ children.

7. Aunt Clare's moods were _____ and likely to swing to extremes.

8. Amy was so tired she practically _____ into bed.

9. The florist's _____ tone of voice made Amy offer to pay for the flower.

10. Aunt Clare arranged for an _____ to look over the furniture and set up an auction.

11. Aunt Clare apologized and said that she had _____ to that business up in the attic.

12. When Amy went to sleep at Aunt Clare's house, Louann felt _____ and alone.

13. Even when Amy closed her eyes, the dollhouse appeared _____ as if it were there in the room.

14. Grandma's arthritis was so bad it made her afraid of becoming an _____ .

15. Amy and Ellen went to the library's _____ area to locate the articles.

Short Answer: Answer the following in one or two brief sentences.

Why didn't Clare like the dollhouse?

Trivia Busters: Answer each of these questions in a short phrase.

1. Which room was the grandmother doll standing in when Amy realized the doll had moved?

2. Where was Amy's father when the murders occurred?

The Dollhouse Murders—Chapters 10-19

Vocabulary: Fill in the blanks with appropriate words taken from the vocabulary lists for Chapters 10-19.

1. Aunt Clare couldn't believe Amy could be so _____ as to gossip about the family secrets to her friends.

2. Aunt Clare had suspected all along that her _____ was the murderer.

3. When the truth was revealed, there was a new _____ and peacefulness about Aunt Clare and the old house.

4. Louann was able to accept Aunt Clare's _____ as long as she didn't embarrass her.

5. Amy was so glad to get out of the attic that she felt almost _____ .

6. Once Louann found out about the slumber party, nothing could _____ her from getting to go.

7. The girls went upstairs while Aunt Clare _____ behind to close up the house for the night.

8. Once Aunt Clare had _____ her suspicions, Amy knew she must uncover the truth.

9. Up in the attic that night the dollhouse lights came on almost _____ and it was easier to see.

10. The title on the book's _____ was "A Doll's House."

11. Aunt Clare said it wasn't good for Louann to be so _____ to getting all the attention.

12. Mother's expression was a funny little _____ when Louann talked about her day at Mrs. Peck's.

13. Rather than ask Aunt Clare for all the painful details, Amy _____ went to the library for information.

14. Her father was like an island of calm in the _____ of family storms.

15. Aunt Clare made sure that Louann was more _____ and calm at the slumber party.

Trivia Busters: Fill in the blanks with one word that would make sense in the context of the story.

1. Aunt Clare said she was a firm believer in the soothing power of a _____ .

2. Amy turned _____ on her birthday.

3. The grandmother doll standing in the parlor was trying to tell Amy something about a letter in a

_____ .

4. The banging noise outside the house was made by _____ .

5. Reuben Miller worked as a _____ and gardener for the Treloars.

     Best Young Adult Novels—Volume 1

Name: _____ Date: _____

Final Test
The Dollhouse Murders

Character Identification: Write the character's name in the blank beside each description of that character. You may use a name more than once.

Louann	Mother	Ellen
Amy	Father	Kathy
Aunt Clare	Grandma Treloar	Mrs. Peck
Grandpa Treloar	Tom Keaton	Reuben Miller

1. _____ Died in a car accident.

2. _____ Was found asleep in the closet.

3. _____ Pushed a desk in front of the parlor door.

4. _____ Looks like she has crayon on her eyebrows.

5. _____ Went out of town to help her friend for a day or two.

6. _____ Taught Louann to make a pot holder.

7. _____ Lost jobs and got headaches.

8. _____ Found the necessary information in the library.

9. _____ Hid the letter in the book.

10. _____ Was a gardener and general handyman.

11. _____ Was charming but hotheaded and drank too much.

12. _____ Was given the dollhouse on her fifteenth birthday.

13. _____ Was starting to resent her sister.

14. _____ Attended a school for exceptional children.

15. _____ Was given the dollhouse by Aunt Clare.

Short Answer: Answer the following in one or two brief sentences.

1. How did Amy know to look in the books for a clue?

2. Describe Aunt Clare's life in Chicago.

Answer Key

The Dollhouse Murders (*Worksheet, Chapters 1–9*)

Vocabulary

1. isolated
2. resentment
3. remote
4. prominent
5. hermit
6. exceptional
7. unpredictable
8. collapsed
9. sarcastic
10. appraiser
11. overreacted
12. abandoned
13. vividly
14. invalid
15. reference

Short Answer (Answers may vary.)

She thought of it as an "expensive beautiful reminder that her grandparents wanted a little girl in their house, not a teenager who was in a hurry to grow up."

Trivia Busters

1. in the parlor
2. in the closet

The Dollhouse Murders (*Worksheet, Chapters 10–19*)

Vocabulary

1. insensitive
2. fiancé
3. serenity
4. reproof
5. giddy
6. sidetrack
7. lingered
8. confided
9. imperceptibly
10. binding
11. accustomed
12. grimace
13. discreetly
14. midst
15. subdued

Trivia Busters

1. snack
2. thirteen
3. book
4. raccoons
5. handyman

Final Test

Character Identification

1. Tom Keaton
2. Father
3. Grandma Treloar
4. Kathy
5. Mother
6. Mrs. Peck
7. Aunt Clare
8. Amy
9. Grandma Treloar
10. Reuben Miller
11. Tom Keaton
12. Aunt Clare
13. Amy
14. Louann
15. Louann

Short Answer (Answers may vary.)

1. The grandmother doll was always found in the parlor, looking at the books.

2. She felt responsible for her grandparents' deaths. She had headaches and couldn't keep a job; she was moody.

Extension Activities

The Dollhouse Murders

Discussion

CHAPTER 1
1. Why was Amy embarrassed?
2. What does Amy assume about Ellen's plans for tomorrow?

CHAPTER 2
1. Why didn't Aunt Clare like the dollhouse?
2. Why has Aunt Clare's return seemed uncomfortable?

CHAPTER 3
1. Why has Aunt Clare returned?
2. How does Aunt Clare expect to get permission for Amy's stay?

CHAPTER 4
1. How does Louann feel about Mrs. Peck?
2. What does Mother do when she's upset?

CHAPTER 5
1. How does Aunt Clare remember her childhood experiences with her grandparents?
2. What upset Amy in the attic?

CHAPTER 6
1. In what way is Aunt Clare different from Amy's mother?
2. How is Aunt Clare unpredictable?

CHAPTER 7
1. Why does Amy go to the library?
2. What did Amy learn from the newspaper about her family?

CHAPTER 8
1. How old was Aunt Clare when the murders took place?
2. What will make Aunt Clare feel like a "new woman"?

CHAPTER 9
1. Does Aunt Clare believe Amy?
2. What does Aunt Clare think her grandparents died thinking?

CHAPTER 10
1. How has Louann's opinion of Mrs. Peck changed?
2. How do Amy and her mother react to the changes Mrs. Peck has made in Louann?

CHAPTER 11
1. What is Aunt Clare's opinion of Louann?
2. What frightened Amy up in the attic?

CHAPTER 12
1. Where does Amy find each of the dolls?
2. What happens that could spoil the party?

CHAPTER 13
1. What does the "Great Zorina" tell Amy?
2. How does Aunt Clare help with Louann?

CHAPTER 14
1. How did Kathy react to Louann?
2. Why does Amy go to the attic?

CHAPTER 15
1. What is Ellen's advice about the dollhouse?
2. Why is Aunt Clare angry?

(continued)

The Dollhouse Murders *(continued)*

CHAPTER 16

1. What does Aunt Clare think happened on the night of the murders?
2. How has that night affected Aunt Clare's life?

CHAPTER 17

1. What do the girls see in the dollhouse?
2. Why did Amy want to go up in the attic this time?

CHAPTER 18

1. What does Aunt Clare do when she's upset?
2. What truth did Aunt Clare learn?

CHAPTER 19

1. How has Aunt Clare changed?
2. Why does Aunt Clare give the dollhouse to Louann?

Reading

1. Students who enjoyed this book may also enjoy these books by the same author:

   Getting Rid of Marjorie   *The Secret Window*

2. Other supernatural mysteries are:

   Ghost Behind Me by Eve Bunting   *Portrait of Jennie* by R. Nathan
   Locked in Time by Lois Duncan   *The Haunting of Safekeep* by Eve Bunting
   Watcher in the Wood   *The Seance* by Joan Lowery Nixon
      by Florence E. Randall   * *Into the Dream* by William Sleator

      * covered in this volume

Writing

1. Have a student committee write a play version of Chapter 13. Include the slumber party as well as the trip up to the attic.

2. In Chapter 19 Amy and Aunt Clare discuss the "family burden." Have students imagine they are Amy and write her journal entry explaining her feelings about her sister at that point.

Research

1. Collecting dollhouse miniatures is one of the most popular hobbies in America today. Have students research this hobby and visit miniature shops in your area.

2. Amy researched the newspaper accounts of the murders of her great-grandparents. Have students use newspaper accounts available in your library to research an unsolved mystery either in your area or at the national level.

Drama

Have a small committee of students dramatize (with scripts) the play version of Chapter 13 they wrote for assignment 1 in the Writing section.

A Gift of Magic

by Lois Duncan

Synopsis

Nancy's family has always traveled around the world to be with her father who works as a foreign correspondent. But when Nancy's mother decides she has had enough of hotels and airplanes, she and the children move back to her Florida childhood home. There, Nancy begins to adjust to her new life-style and explores her special gift of ESP.

Vocabulary

CHAPTER 1
1. sensations
2. the Riviera
3. currents
4. correspondent

CHAPTER 2
1. seminar
2. poised
3. improvise
4. tranquil
5. nondescript
6. solitaire
7. dominated
8. dynamic
9. reluctant

CHAPTER 3
1. anticipation
2. harried
3. diminished

CHAPTER 4
1. contemporaries
2. clique
3. predetermined
4. perplexity
5. convenient

CHAPTER 5
1. impertinence
2. extrasensory perception
3. consistent

CHAPTER 6
1. phobia
2. gamaphobia
3. haptophobia
4. enthusiastic
5. psychic
6. phenomena

CHAPTER 7
1. telepathy
2. clairvoyance
3. precognition
4. retrocognition

CHAPTER 8
1. custody
2. vehement
3. engrossed

CHAPTER 9
1. dainty
2. appropriate
3. agony

CHAPTER 10
1. protruding
2. potential
3. garment

CHAPTER 11
1. paragon
2. disconcerting
3. faculty

CHAPTER 12
1. apprehension
2. radiant
3. belated
4. insolence
5. volition
6. amended
7. contagious

CHAPTER 13
1. anesthetic
2. orthopedic
3. reassure

CHAPTER 14
1. truancy
2. casualties
3. enchanted

CHAPTER 15
1. appraise
2. exertion
3. contemplate

CHAPTER 16
1. irresistible
2. materialize
3. endure
4. diffused

A Gift of Magic—Chapters 1-6

Vocabulary: Fill in the blanks with appropriate words from the vocabulary lists for Chapters 1-6.

1. All of Nancy's _____ told her that Tom Duncan was different from anyone else.

2. Mr. Garrett had a very _____ personality.

3. Elizabeth's personality was _____ by her husband's.

4. Elizabeth didn't want Brendon to swim alone because of the strong ocean

   _____ .

5. Mr. Garrett worked as a foreign _____ .

6. Kirby could _____ a dance to any music.

7. Madame Vilar was a very _____ and graceful woman.

8. Nancy and her grandmother both have powers of _____ .

9. Nancy was well traveled and loved reading, so she had a broader background than most of

   her _____ .

10. Greg's parents thought that poking around in his workshop might give him a

    _____ .

11. Madame thought it strange that someone with no _____ training could dance as well as Kirby.

12. Miss Green said she wouldn't stand for Kirby's _____ .

13. The girls at school all seemed to belong to cliques _____ the year before.

14. Brendon liked to play _____ right in front of his sister's bedroom door.

15. The crowd of students in the halls had _____ before Greg and Brendon's fight.

Short Answer: Answer the following questions in complete sentences.

1. Why are Nancy's parents getting divorced?

2. What was the difference between the way the two sisters handled the news of the divorce?

Name: _____ Date: _____

A *Gift of Magic*—Chapters 7–16

Vocabulary: Fill in the blanks with appropriate words taken from the vocabulary lists for Chapters 7–16.

1. Brendon says it is pure _____ for him to have to listen to Nancy play the piano.

2. Nancy felt that it wasn't _____ for Mr. Duncan to give her mother the locket.

3. The _____ turned out to be an old-fashioned christening gown that Kirby must have worn.

4. With her grades, Nancy looked like some sort of _____ compared to Kirby and Brendon.

5. Miss Green had not been well and was in no mood to tolerate _____ from Nancy.

6. The giggle seemed _____ among the students, and soon they were all laughing at Miss Green.

7. Kirby was given an _____ to dull her pain.

8. Mother said that for Kirby to stay home any longer would be _____ and she couldn't allow it.

9. Brendon saw Greg's face turn red from _____ as he carried the boat's stern to the water.

10. The thought of not dancing was almost more than Kirby could _____ .

Short Answer: Answer the following questions in complete sentences.

1. Why was the locket a special gift to Elizabeth?

2. What did Nancy talk her mother into doing with the locket? Why?

3. How does Nancy cheat on the card experiment? Why?

4. Why doesn't Kirby get the lead in the ballet?

5. What did Kirby notice about Tom Duncan after the ballet?

Name: _____ Date: _____

Final Test
A Gift of Magic

Character Identification: Write the character's letter in the blank next to each description of that character. Use letters as many times as necessary.

(a) Brendon   (d) Richard Garrett   (g) Greg

(b) Madame Vilar   (e) Tom Duncan   (h) Kirby

(c) Elizabeth Garrett   (f) Nancy   (i) Grandmother

1. _____ Works as a foreign correspondent.

2. _____ Isn't paid in money for Kirby's lessons.

3. _____ Helped Brendon build the boat.

4. _____ Gave Elizabeth two lockets.

5. _____ She knew Richard and Elizabeth weren't right together.

6. _____ Worked as a school counselor.

7. _____ Wanted to teach Miss Green a lesson.

8. _____ Left the house to Elizabeth.

9. _____ She seemed dominated by her husband's personality.

10. _____ Felt responsible for Kirby's accident.

11. _____ Told Kirby to build her life in other directions.

12. _____ Was married to a mathematics professor.

13. _____ Cheated on Dr. Russo's experiment.

14. _____ Had been dieting.

15. _____ Wanted Greg to help find buried treasure.

16. _____ Loved children's stories and fairy tales.

17. _____ Found the christening gown in the attic.

18. _____ Bought the black swan on impulse.

19. _____ Thought it best to send Kirby back to school.

20. _____ Went to London and became famous.

21. _____ Thought reading music was a waste of time.

22. _____ Had to write 500 times about laughing at others.

23. _____ Grew up and had five children.

24. _____ Thought he would never marry again.

Answer Key

A Gift of Magic (Worksheet, Chapters 1–6)

Vocabulary

1. sensations
2. dynamic
3. dominated
4. currents
5. correspondent
6. improvise
7. poised
8. extrasensory perception
9. contemporaries
10. phobia
11. consistent
12. impertinence
13. predetermined
14. solitaire
15. diminished

Short Answer (Answers may vary.)

1. Elizabeth Garrett wants to settle into a real home and not move around so much. She wants her own life.

2. Nancy couldn't accept it and wanted to believe her parents would get back together again. Kirby understood that her mother wasn't happy before; she understood the divorce.

A Gift of Magic (Worksheet, Chapters 7–16)

Vocabulary

1. agony
2. appropriate
3. garment
4. paragon
5. insolence
6. contagious
7. anesthetic
8. truancy
9. exertion
10. endure

Short Answer (Answers may vary.)

1. She was given a necklace like the locket a long time ago by Tom Duncan, but lost the first one.

2. Nancy asked her mother to give it back to Tom Duncan, at least until summer when her father visits. Nancy hoped her parents would get back together.

3. She purposely calls all the wrong answers. She is afraid she will become some sort of freak with ESP.

4. There is only one boy dancer who would not be able to pick Kirby up in the ballet.

5. Kirby noticed that he was in love with her mother (Elizabeth).

Final Test

Character Identification

1. d	7. f	13. f	19. c
2. b	8. i	14. h	20. h
3. g	9. c	15. a	21. a
4. e	10. f	16. c	22. f
5. i	11. e	17. f	23. f
6. e	12. b	18. h	24. d

Extension Activities

A Gift of Magic

Discussion

PROLOGUE

1. What gifts did Grandmother leave?
2. In what way are her gifts unusual?

CHAPTER 1

1. Why has the family come to Florida?
2. What is the conflict between Nancy's parents?

CHAPTER 2

1. Describe Richard Garrett's personality.
2. What unusual talent does Nancy have?
3. Why is it more difficult for Nancy to be happy about the move?

CHAPTER 3

1. Describe Greg Russo.
2. How do Greg and Brendon become friends?

CHAPTER 4

1. Why were Nancy and Kirby in the same grade at school?
2. What kind of job did Elizabeth get and why?
3. Why does Miss Green think Nancy cheated?

CHAPTER 5

1. Why does Madame Vilar remind Kirby of a swan?
2. How does Kirby feel about Nancy's "gift"?
3. Why doesn't Kirby look like a dancer?

CHAPTER 6

1. In what way is Greg's home life unusual?
2. How did Brendon reveal Nancy's gift to Dr. Russo?

CHAPTER 7

1. In what strange way is Nancy making friends in her geography class?
2. Why doesn't she change to another geography class?
3. How does Brendon respond to Nancy's piano playing?

CHAPTER 8

1. Why didn't Kirby get the lead in the Nutcracker ballet?
2. How does Kirby describe her mother's life here in Florida?
3. What does Nancy realize about Mr. Duncan?

CHAPTER 9

1. Why is this the first "real" Christmas for the Garrett children?
2. Why did Mr. Duncan buy Elizabeth a locket?
3. What promise does Elizabeth make Nancy?

CHAPTER 10

1. What does Nancy plan to do with the christening gown?
2. How did Nancy "meet" her grandmother?

CHAPTER 11

1. What doesn't Kirby like about this new attitude of Nancy's?
2. How does Madame get paid for Kirby's lessons?
3. Why was Kirby's gift very important to Madame?

(continued)

118

CHAPTER 12

1. Describe Maggie Courtney.
2. How does Nancy feel about Kirby's interest in Ballet South?
3. What did Nancy do to get even with Miss Green?

CHAPTER 13

1. In what way does Kirby's attitude change after the accident?
2. How does Nancy feel about the accident?

CHAPTER 14

1. Why won't Nancy use her gift any longer?
2. In what way does Brendon use his gift?
3. Why does Elizabeth decide to send Kirby back to school?
4. How did Grandmother feel about Richard Garrett?

CHAPTER 15

1. Describe Brendon's boat.
2. How do the boys get separated?

CHAPTER 16

1. Why was Nancy home alone?
2. What news came in the letter?
3. How does Nancy learn that Brendon is in trouble?

CHAPTER 17

1. What happened to Greg?
2. In what way did the card test backfire on Nancy?
3. How does Mr. Duncan help Nancy understand her "powers"?

EPILOGUE

1. How do each of the children use their gifts?

Reading

1. Lois Duncan often uses variations on the ESP theme in many of her young adult novels. Other books by Ms. Duncan that incorporate ESP or the supernatural are:

   Down a Dark Hall
   * *Killing Mr. Griffin*
   * *Stranger With My Face*

   * *The Third Eye*
   Locked in Time
   Summer of Fear

   * covered in Volume III of this series

2. Lois Duncan specializes in young adult mysteries. The following books all are high-interest mysteries for young people:

   Daughters of Eve
   * *I Know What You Did Last Summer*
   Ransom (also titled *Five Were Missing*)

   They Never Came Home
   Don't Look Behind You

   * covered in Volume III of this series

Writing

1. In many ways this book contains many fairy-tale qualities, with a grandmother bestowing powerful gifts and even a "happily ever after" at the end. Have students write their own personal fairy tale. Have a character bestow a gift of a specific talent. How would the gift be used?

(continued)

A *Gift of Magic* (continued)

2. In Chapter 16, Nancy reads the letter from her father telling his children that he has remarried. Have students write a letter from Nancy to her father showing how her attitude and hopes have changed.

3. Although this book has an epilogue, it isn't very detailed in its information about relationships. Have students write a sequel (or short chapter) in which Nancy explains to her half-sister Lois about their grandmother's gifts.

Research

1. Students interested in further information concerning ESP could research the following topics:

   clairvoyance   telepathy
   precognition/retrocognition   hyperkinesis

2. Another interesting facet of the topic would be to research the life of Edgar Cayce, America's most famous psychic. Students could report on his life and perhaps his impact on current attitudes concerning ESP.

Art

Have students draw or illustrate the following scenes: (1) Nancy in the attic talking to Grandmother, (2) Kirby dancing, (3) Nancy reaching out in her mind to each of her family members and hearing Brendon's call for help.

Drama

Have students rewrite in play form and act out the scene in the car with Nancy Kirby and Tom Duncan (Chapter 14).

Video

A VCR tape entitled "A Visit With Lois Duncan" is available (17 minutes). For information, write RDA Enterprises, 1112 Dakota NE, Albuquerque, NM 87110.

The Indian in the Cupboard
by Lynne Reid Banks

Synopsis

The story begins with a plain cupboard, a plastic Indian figure, and an ornate key that somehow unlocks the magic. For Omri, the plastic Indian figure was hardly the birthday gift he had imagined. When the figure comes to life inside the cupboard, Omri enters into a whole new world of responsibility, wonder, and magic that involves an Iroquois Indian named Little Bear and an American cowboy from the late 1880's named Boone.

Vocabulary

CHAPTER 1
1. petrified
2. coherent
3. vast
4. plait
5. minuscule
6. torso
7. bandelier

CHAPTER 2
1. tantalizing
2. appalled
3. coaxed
4. ravenous
5. fragile

CHAPTER 3
1. intense
2. uncompromising
3. stability
4. lithely
5. genie

CHAPTER 4
1. peril

CHAPTER 5
1. ado
2. wielding

CHAPTER 6
1. dire
2. hectoring

CHAPTER 7
1. uncanny
2. galvanized
3. stench

CHAPTER 8
1. mulish
2. gingerly
3. doggedly
4. aghast

CHAPTER 9
1. tethered
2. relish
3. prostrate
4. scornful

CHAPTER 10
1. truce
2. nonplused
3. pummeling

CHAPTER 11
1. apprehension
2. chaos
3. fiendish
4. raucous

CHAPTER 12
1. gesticulating

CHAPTER 13
1. infinitesimal
2. stupefaction

CHAPTER 14
1. sieve
2. novelty
3. restive
4. chasm

CHAPTER 15
1. joist

CHAPTER 16
1. stealthily
2. relapse

Name: _____   Date: _____

The Indian in the Cupboard—Chapters 1-8

Vocabulary: Using your knowledge of the vocabulary words and the book, answer the following with a character's name or object.

1. Who was petrified the first time he heard something moving in the cupboard?

   _____

2. Who had a habit of being very mulish? _____

3. What object was Omri's plastic knight wielding? _____

4. Who always seemed to be ravenous? _____

5. Who wore a bandelier across his torso? _____

6. In Little Bear's eyes, who would have been the genie? _____

7. Who wore a plait down his back? _____

8. Without much ado, who quickly and quietly treated Little Bear's wounds?

   _____

9. Who didn't realize the peril of bringing Little Bear and Boone to school?

   _____

10. Who coaxed Omri into changing the plastic cowboy into a real persson?

   _____

Character Identification: Write the character's letter in the blank next to each description of that character. You may use a letter more than once.

(a) Omri   (c) Little Bear   (e) Boone

(b) Patrick   (d) Tommy

1. _____ Didn't think a plastic figure was such a neat birthday present at first.
2. _____ Omri's best friend.
3. _____ Thinks that Omri is just a dream.
4. _____ Nicknamed "Boohoo."
5. _____ Iroquois warrior.
6. _____ Injured by kicking horse.
7. _____ A medic.
8. _____ Given an old key by his mother.
9. _____ He is surprised when shot by Boone in the face.
10. _____ Has two brothers.

The Indian in the Cupboard—Chapters 9–16

Character Description: Fill in the chart below with the appropriate information about each character.

CHARACTER	FROM WHAT TIME?	PLACE OF ORIGIN	GENERAL PERSONALITY
Omri			
Patrick			
Little Bear			
Boone			
Tommy			
Bright Stars			

Vocabulary: Fill in the blanks with words from the list below.

infinitesimal   truce   prostrate
sieve   stealthily
tethered   relapse

1. Boone kept pretending to have a _____ in order to get everyone's sympathy.

2. Slowly, almost _____ , Bright Stars emerged from the cupboard.

3. Omri insisted that Boone and Little Bear make a _____ .

4. They _____ the horse to a twig.

5. Boone's _____ body lay quietly, not moving.

6. They decided to _____ the sand, hoping to find the key.

7. The art teacher couldn't believe how _____ Omri's drawing was.

Name: _____ Date: _____

Final Test
The Indian in the Cupboard

Multiple Choice: Choose the one best answer to each of the following. Write the letter of that choice in the blank.

1. _____ Omri received the plastic Indian from   (a) Patrick   (b) his older brother   (c) his parents   (d) Tommy.

2. _____ Omri received the old cupboard from   (a) Patrick   (b) his brother   (c) his parents   (d) Tommy.

3. _____ Instead of a teepee, Little Bear wanted a(n)   (a) igloo   (b) hogan   (c) sweathouse   (d) longhouse.

4. _____ The Iroquois fought beside the   (a) English   (b) French   (c) Americans   (d) Spanish.

5. _____ Little Bear wasn't too impressed with the   (a) meat   (b) Coke   (c) bread and cheese   (d) ice cream.

6. _____ Omri's father was angry with him for taking the   (a) food from the refrigerator   (b) seed tray   (c) sweater   (d) keys.

7. _____ Instead of a plastic figure, Patrick thought Omri would be more excited by his new   (a) baseball bat   (b) bicycle   (c) motorized car   (d) skateboard.

8. _____ When Omri came home and found his brothers in his room, they were fascinated with   (a) Little Bear   (b) the longhouse   (c) the little horse   (d) the cupboard.

9. _____ Patrick was surprised when his cowboy   (a) started shouting at him   (b) shot him in the face   (c) knifed him   (d) started singing.

10. _____ Who calls Omri and Patrick a "hallucy-nation"?   (a) Little Bear   (b) Tommy   (c) Bright Stars   (d) Boone

11. _____ Boone is known for his   (a) cruelty   (b) laugh   (c) soft heart   (d) big appetite.

12. _____ During Omri's art class, Boone drew a picture of   (a) his hometown   (b) himself   (c) his horse   (d) Little Bear.

13. _____ Even though Omri didn't want him to, who did Patrick show the live figures to?   (a) Omri's brother   (b) Mr. Johnson   (c) Patrick's mother   (d) the art teacher

14. _____ Who actually chose Bright Stars?   (a) Patrick   (b) Omri   (c) Mr. Yapp   (d) Little Bear

15. _____ In England, Toffo is   (a) a cookie   (b) a type of meat   (c) a kind of candy   (d) a type of cheese.

16. _____ What got loose in Omri's room that could have killed Little Bear and Boone?   (a) the horses   (b) a rat   (c) a hamster   (d) a cat

17. _____ The only way that Omri got out of the shoplifting accusation was when   (a) his mother stuck up for him   (b) his brothers offered to pay for the figures   (c) Little Bear and Boone pretended to be fake figures   (d) Patrick took the figures and put them in his pocket.

18. _____ Who, in a fit of rage, hid Omri's cupboard from him?   (a) Patrick   (b) Adiel   (c) Little Bear   (d) Omri's mother

19. _____ Tommy couldn't administer penicillin to Boone because   (a) Boone said he was allergic to it   (b) Tommy didn't have any more with him   (c) it hadn't been invented yet   (d) he didn't have a needle.

20. _____ For safekeeping, Omri   (a) gives the key to his mother   (b) gives the key to Little Bear   (c) hides the key in the backyard   (d) takes the key to school and puts it in his desk.

Answer Key

The Indian in the Cupboard (*Worksheet, Chapters 1–8*)

Vocabulary

1. Omri	3. an axe	5. Little Bear	7. Little Bear	9. Patrick
2. Little Bear (or Patrick)	4. Little Bear	6. Omri	8. Tommy	10. Patrick

Character Identification

1. a	3. d	5. c	7. d	9. b
2. b	4. e	6. c	8. a	10. a

The Indian in the Cupboard (*Worksheet, Chapters 9–16*)

Character Description (Answers may vary.)

CHARACTER	FROM WHAT TIME?	PLACE OF ORIGIN	GENERAL PERSONALITY
Omri	Present day	England	More mature than some his age; sees the responsibility of keeping Little Bear.
Patrick	Present day	England	More stubborn than Omri; not as responsible but still understanding at times.
Little Bear	Probably late 1700's or early 1800's	East Coast of U.S.	Very stubborn and demanding; proud and extremely brave.
Boone	Late 1800's	Western U.S.	Very sensitive, proud; not concerned with cleanliness.
Tommy	Early 1900's	Europe (England)	Agreeable person; easy to get along with; willing to help others.
Bright Stars	Not sure*	United States	Quiet, wary, accepting.

* Not much is said about Bright Stars, but since she and Little Bear seem to accept each other so readily, one might assume that they came from the same time period and spoke a similar language.

(continued)

The Indian in the Cupboard (continued)

Vocabulary

1. relapse
2. stealthily
3. truce
4. tethered
5. prostrate
6. sieve
7. infinitesimal

Final Test

Multiple Choice

1. a	5. c	9. b	13. b	17. c
2. b	6. b	10. d	14. d	18. b
3. d	7. d	11. c	15. c	19. c
4. a	8. b	12. a	16. b	20. a

Extension Activities

The Indian in the Cupboard

Discussion

CHAPTER 1
1. Why was Omri a little disappointed at first with his plastic Indian?
2. What has magically seemed to happen with the cupboard and the key?

CHAPTER 2
1. Why did Omri almost tell his secret to Patrick?
2. At what times does Little Bear seem disgusted with Omri?

CHAPTER 3
1. How did Omri double-check the "magic" of the cupboard?
2. Why wouldn't Little Bear sleep in the beautiful teepee made from plastic?
3. Why didn't Omri tell any adults about Little Bear?

CHAPTER 4
1. Why is the outdoors potentially dangerous to Little Bear and the horse?
2. What other person has Omri brought to life? Why?

CHAPTER 5
1. Why does Little Bear want a longhouse? What exactly is a longhouse?
2. How did Omri get an axe for Little Bear?

CHAPTER 6
1. Why was it important for Omri to go to the library?
2. How did Little Bear become a chief?

CHAPTER 7
1. Why would it be impractical to turn all Omri's plastic figures to life?

2. How is Little Bear a bit unreasonable at times?

CHAPTER 8
1. Who has now been brought to life? Why?
2. How might Patrick really complicate matters?

CHAPTER 9
1. What is Boone's nickname? What does that tell you about him?
2. What might happen when Omri takes Little Bear to school?

CHAPTER 10
1. How did Omri start to make friends out of Little Bear and Boone?

CHAPTER 11
1. What was school like for Little Bear and Boone?
2. How could Little Bear and Boone have been killed?

CHAPTER 12
1. What did Omri find out about human greed?
2. How did Patrick jeopardize Little Bear's and Boone's lives?

CHAPTER 13
1. Why is Patrick and Omri's friendship being tested at this time? Is there anything they can do to make it stronger?
2. How did Omri play a joke on his art teacher?
3. How did Patrick save Omri at Yapp's?

(continued)

127

CHAPTER 14

1. How does Little Bear's happiness become more important than Omri's?

2. What incident has caused Little Bear shame? Why?

CHAPTER 15

1. Why did Patrick and Omri feel they had to stay up all night?

2. Why was Tommy brought back again?

CHAPTER 16

1. Why did Omri decide to send all of them back to their own worlds?

2. What final ceremony is done for Boone and Little Bear? Why?

Reading

1. If students like this book, they will love the two sequels: *The Return of the Indian* and *The Secret of the Indian* by the same author, Lynne Reid Banks.

2. Other books by Lynne Reid Banks are:

   I, Houdini: The Autobiography of a Self-Educated Hamster
   The Fairy Rebel
   Melusine (for mature readers only)

3. There are several good books involving Native Americans. Students interested in reading more about Native Americans might like some of these choices:

   When the Legends Die by Hal Borland
   Only Earth and Sky Last Forever
      by Nathaniel Benchley
   Shadi by Margaret Embry
   Laughing Boy by Oliver La Farge
   Light in the Forest by Conrad Richter

   Streams to the River, River to the Sea
      by Scott O'Dell
   The Ordeal of Running Standing
      by Thomas Fall
   Jenny of the Tetons
      by Kristiana Gregory

Writing

1. Write a report on the Iroquois Indians, using what you read in the book and also what you can find in other reference books.

2. Become Boone and go back to the late 1800's. Write an article for the newspaper (back then) telling about all the future inventions that you had witnessed.

3. Tommy has always thought he was just having a dream when he went into Omri's world. Imagine that Tommy keeps a diary; write in diary form the two "dreams" that he has experienced.

4. As readers, we have not really heard Bright Stars speak about herself. Write an autobiography (as if you were Bright Stars) giving her background, tribe, language, first reaction to Little Bear, etc.

(continued)

Research

1. Students could pair up and study different Native American tribes and report to the class on their findings. Included in the reports should be history of the tribe, language spoken, leaders, and customs.

2. There are some outstanding Native American leaders that students could read about and report on. Here is a list of just some of the outstanding leaders:

Chief Joseph (Nez Perce)	Tecumseh (Shawnee)
Chief Seattle (Dwamish)	Sitting Bull (Sioux)
Black Elk (Oglala Sioux)	Roman Nose (Cheyenne)
Red Jacket (Seneca)	Sun Chief (Hopi)
Crazy Horse (Oglala Sioux)	Black Hawk (Sauk & Fox)
Manuelito (Navajo)	Geronimo (Apache)

3. Have the class research words in the English language that relate back to Native American words. Also, the class could study the United States (or just one state) and discuss the places that are named for Native American tribes or words.

4. Many times in *The Indian in the Cupboard* Omri realized he had the wrong concept of Indians because of the movies he had seen. Have students view different movies depicting Native Americans and see if they can find the fallacies in the films. (Individuals or groups of students could be assigned the viewing of a certain film.) Have the class decide on the most accurate film portraying Native Americans and the worst film.

Art

1. Assign groups to construct a teepee and a longhouse. Discuss the differences and point out advantages and disadvantages of both types of lodgings.

2. There are books that describe handmade crafts of some of the Native Americans. Class members might want to check one out of the library and make some of the crafts mentioned.

Drama

1. Many of the scenes could be acted out, especially the one where Patrick and Omri are in the principal's office or at Yapp's when Omri is accused of shoplifting.

2. Have students write the scene that must have happened when Boone went back to his own time and had to check in with the doctor about his wound.

From the Mixed-Up Files of Mrs. Basil E. Frankweiler
by E. L. Konigsburg

Synopsis

Claudia decides to run away in order to teach her family a lesson in "Claudia Appreciation." She only invites her younger brother Jamie because he has the money to finance the adventure. Claudia masterminds every detail of running away to stay at the Metropolitan Museum of Art. Her successful plan leads the two children into another adventure—discovering the art of Michelangelo.

Vocabulary

CHAPTER 1
1. knapsack
2. calculated
3. suburbs
4. injustice
5. monotony
6. Mah-Jongg
7. ventured
8. accustomed
9. Neanderthal
10. erupted
11. tyrannies
12. tycoon
13. cautious
14. boodle

CHAPTER 2
1. percolator
2. punctuated
3. penetrated
4. stowaways
5. expenditures

CHAPTER 3
1. collapse
2. fatigue
3. mutual
4. consulting
5. mimicked
6. inconspicuous
7. destination
8. condemned
9. chancellor of the exchequer
10. veto
11. canopy
12. ornately
13. fussbudget
14. corridors
15. extravagant

CHAPTER 4
1. essence
2. elegance
3. sarcophagus
4. tapestry
5. urn
6. emerge
7. ambitions
8. Renaissance
9. barrier
10. vain
11. chartered
12. imposter
13. embalm
14. acquisitions
15. Michelangelo
16. Leonardo da Vinci
17. abroad
18. Bologna, Italy
19. hodgepodge
20. mediocre
21. integrity

CHAPTER 5
1. executive
2. pagan
3. accumulate
4. pedestal
5. corpuscle
6. telepathy

CHAPTER 6
1. stealthily

CHAPTER 7
1. muzzle

CHAPTER 8
1. abrasions
2. topaz
3. counterfeit
4. consensus
5. sarcastic
6. heroine
7. self-assurance

CHAPTER 9
1. paupers
2. baroque
3. emitted
4. sauntered
5. muted
6. sonnet
7. authenticity

CHAPTER 10
1. accurate
2. bequeathing

From the Mixed-Up Files of Mrs. Basil E. Frankweiler—**Chapters 1–5**

Vocabulary: Fill in the blanks with appropriate words or names taken from the vocabulary lists for Chapters 1–5.

1. The statue was placed on a _____ .

2. Some people considered Mrs. Frankweiler's collection a _____ of the great and the mediocre.

3. The other students in the class knew Jamie was an _____ .

4. Jamie said that for a sister and a _____ , Claudia wasn't too bad.

5. Claudia said that wearing shoes was one of the _____ Jamie would escape by running away.

6. Claudia was tired of the family injustices and the _____ of the same old things.

7. Jamie tried to use mental _____ to signal Claudia to stay put.

8. Claudia said that cupids had bows and arrows and were _____ , too.

9. "Angel" was one of the museum's most recent _____ .

10. The statue has been studied by art experts at the museum as well as experts

    _____ .

11. Mrs. Frankweiler claims to have purchased the statue from a dealer in

    _____ , before the war.

12. Jamie chose the galleries of the Italian _____ because he thought Claudia would be bored.

13. Claudia hid her violin case in a _____ that had no lid.

14. The draperies on the _____ bed helped to hide them from the night watchman.

15. As the one in charge of money, Jamie considered himself as their _____ .

16. Jamie reminded Claudia she had no more income and so could no longer be

    _____ .

Short Answer: Answer the following question in one or two complete sentences.

What intrigues Claudia about the statue?

From the Mixed-Up Files of Mrs. Basil E. Frankweiler—**Chapters 6-10**

Vocabulary: Fill in the blanks with appropriate words taken from the vocabulary lists for Chapters 6-10.

1. If the reply letter had been nasty or _____ , she could have been righteously angry.

2. The children had to walk _____ up the stairway to avoid the night watchman.

3. Once she found the file, Claudia slowly _____ over to the table.

4. Mrs. Frankweiler wanted Jamie's story on tape to be _____ , but she also wanted him to finish.

5. Mrs. Frankweiler didn't doubt the _____ of the sketch.

6. She wanted the lawyer to rewrite her will _____ the sketch to the children.

7. To get her attention, Jamie _____ two false sneezes.

8. Mrs. Frankweiler was wearing a white lab coat and her _____ pearl necklace.

9. Claudia said she had no idea she wanted to be a _____ when their adventure began.

10. She said she shouldn't be called "Lady Claudia" now that their money was gone and they were _____ .

11. She felt better as the train traveled closer to Mrs. Frankweiler's estate and her _____ returned to her.

12. The letter said that the problem of Angel had become a matter for _____ on the part of experts.

Trivia Busters: Fill in the blanks with details from the book.

1. Translated, "nouilles et fromage" means _____ .

2. Claudia realized the file might be labeled: _____ .

3. Michelangelo's last name was _____ .

4. When she went to freshen up, Claudia ended up _____ .

5. Mrs. Frankweiler promised the children a ride home in a _____ .

6. The museum purchased the statue at an auction for _____ .

7. Saxonberg turns out to be the children's _____ .

8. Mrs. Frankweiler said that eyes were _____ .

Name: _____   Date: _____

Final Test
From the Mixed-Up Files of Mrs. Basil E. Frankweiler

Character Identification: Write the character's name in the blank next to each description of that character. You may use a name more than once.

Claudia   Morris
Saxonberg   Angel
Jamie   Sheldon
Mrs. Frankweiler   Michelangelo

1. _____ Closed the estate three years ago.

2. _____ Sold for $225.00.

3. _____ Tried to eat the list of instructions.

4. _____ The chauffeur.

5. _____ Purchased in Bologna, Italy.

6. _____ Didn't want experts making a science of it.

7. _____ Enjoys complications.

8. _____ Fussbudget.

9. _____ Resembled someone in Claudia's family.

10. _____ Museum guard.

11. _____ Nose is getting longer—like Pinocchio.

12. _____ Tightwad.

13. _____ Signature was three connecting circles and an initial.

14. _____ Wore a white lab coat and baroque pearls.

15. _____ Grandfather.

16. _____ Mailed two box tops and a letter to Mom and Dad.

17. _____ Can be absolutely charming when trying to get information.

18. _____ Honest about everything except cards.

19. _____ Enjoys planning.

20. _____ Was instructed to change the will.

21. _____ Wrote a sonnet next to the sketch.

22. _____ Won the statue in an honest game of cards.

23. _____ Eighty-two years old.

Answer Key

From the Mixed-Up Files of Mrs. Basil E. Frankweiler (*Worksheet, Chapters 1–5*)

Vocabulary

1. pedestal
2. hodgepodge
3. imposter
4. fussbudget
5. tyrannies
6. monotony
7. telepathy
8. pagan
9. acquisitions
10. abroad
11. Bologna, Italy
12. Renaissance
13. sarcophagus
14. canopy
15. chancellor of the exchequer
16. extravagant

Short Answer (Answers may vary.)

The statue is beautiful and graceful and bears a resemblance to someone in her family. There was a "mystery" about the piece.

From the Mixed-Up Files of Mrs. Basil E. Frankweiler (*Worksheet, Chapters 6–10*)

Vocabulary

1. sarcastic
2. stealthily
3. sauntered
4. accurate
5. authenticity
6. bequeathing
7. emitted
8. baroque
9. heroine
10. paupers
11. self-assurance
12. consensus

Trivia Busters

1. macaroni (noodles) and cheese
2. Bologna, Italy
3. Buonarroti
4. taking a bath
5. Rolls Royce
6. $225.00
7. grandfather
8. windows of the soul

Character Identification

1. Mrs. Frankweiler
2. Angel
3. Jamie
4. Sheldon
5. Angel
6. Mrs. Frankweiler
7. Jamie
8. Claudia
9. Angel
10. Morris
11. Mrs. Frankweiler
12. Jamie
13. Michelangelo
14. Mrs. Frankweiler
15. Saxonberg
16. Claudia
17. Mrs. Frankweiler
18. Jamie
19. Claudia
20. Saxonberg
21. Michelangelo
22. Mrs. Frankweiler
23. Mrs. Frankweiler

Extension Activities

From the Mixed-Up Files of Mrs. Basil E. Frankweiler

Discussion

CHAPTER 1

1. Why does Claudia want to run away?
2. Why does Jamie agree to go too?
3. How does Jamie increase his allowance?

CHAPTER 2

1. How did Claudia and Jamie make their getaway?
2. What is Jamie's responsibility during this adventure?
3. What did Claudia put in the mail?

CHAPTER 3

1. How did Claudia and Jamie become a "team"?
2. How did the children stay in the musuem after it closed?

CHAPTER 4

1. What intrigues Claudia about the statue?
2. What does Mrs. Frankweiler mean about "being part of a group"?

CHAPTER 5

1. How do the children get an "income"?
2. How did Claudia get Jamie to the restaurant?

CHAPTER 6

1. How did the children discover the stonemason's mark?

CHAPTER 7

1. What was Jamie's "perfect cover" to deliver the letter?

CHAPTER 8

1. What made Claudia think of going to Farmington?
2. Why didn't Claudia want to go home yet?

CHAPTER 9

1. How did Claudia know where to look for the file?
2. How will Mrs. Frankweiler insure that the children keep her secret?
3. Why doesn't Mrs. Frankweiler want to donate the sketch to the museum?

CHAPTER 10

1. How did Sheldon overhear the children's conversation?
2. What else do you think might be in those mixed-up files?

(continued)

From the Mixed-Up Files of Mrs. Basil E. Frankweiler (continued)

Reading

1. Students who enjoyed this book may enjoy these others by the same author, E. L. Konigsburg:

   About the B'Nai Bagels
   The Second Mrs. Giaconda
   Father's Arcane Daughter
   Jennifer, Hecate, Macbeth, William
      McKinley and Me, Elizabeth

   The Dragon in the Ghetto Caper
   George
   A Proud Taste for Scarlett and Miniver
   Journey to an 800 Number
   Throwing Shadows

2. Two books that explore the possibility of young people hiding out in established places are *The Secrets of the Shopping Mall* by Richard Peck and *Cave Under the City* by Harry Mazer. The latter is covered in this volume.

Writing

1. Write a newspaper article explaining how the children were found and where they were for a week.

2. Write a short story, becoming the author of the book. Where would *you* have selected to stay? How could you go undetected?

3. Write the author a letter asking any questions you may have and telling her what you enjoyed about this book.

Research

1. Research Michelangelo. What were his contributions to the art world? What is known about him personally?

2. Research the Italian Renaissance. Why is this an important period of time in art history?

3. Research the Metropolitan Museum of Art. How did it begin? What kinds of art are available to the public there today?

Art

Imagine the scene where Claudia and Jamie see Angel for the first time. Illustrate the scene.

FANTASY/
SCIENCE FICTION

The Green Book

by Jill Paton Walsh

Synopsis

A small group of people escape Earth's final disaster in order to start life anew on a strange and distant planet. As the colonists explore the planet's resources, they test their own in efforts to survive. It is the children who discover both the wondrous and the practical gifts their new home has to offer.

Vocabulary

CHAPTER 1
1. intermediate
2. treacle
3. diminish
4. navigating
5. void
6. luxury
7. colonization
8. allocated
9. destination

CHAPTER 2
1. engulfing
2. crescent
3. symmetrical
4. inverted
5. marcasite
6. pewter
7. ointment
8. flagons
9. obscuring
10. invigorating
11. isolated

CHAPTER 3
1. amphitheater
2. glacial
3. crystalline
4. unpalatable
5. biorhythms
6. coincidence
7. rations
8. contriver
9. fodder
10. contribution

CHAPTER 4
1. relevant
2. zombie
3. coggled
4. transparent
5. crimson

CHAPTER 5
1. malfunction
2. chrysalis
3. hostile

CHAPTER 6
1. intense
2. bemused
3. rapt
4. random
5. scudding
6. hexagonal
7. agony

CHAPTER 7
1. bunker
2. hankering
3. refugees

Name: _____   Date: _____

The Green Book—Chapters 1-3

Vocabulary: Using just the vocabulary words given below, fill in the blanks with words that would be appropriate within the context of the story.

intermediate	diminish	flagons
glacial	crystalline	contriver
invigorating	luxury	ointment
amphitheater	biorhythms	void
unpalatable	symmetrical	destination

1. Father called the valley a natural _____ full of rocks.

2. Beyond the lake a mountain rose in perfectly _____ slopes topped with snow.

3. Someone was sent to fetch _____ because the grass and flowers had cut our feet.

4. Through the porthole, the earth began to _____ until it looked like a glass marble.

5. Father carefully selected his book titled A *Dictionary of* _____ *Technology.*

6. Even though the jellyfish looked _____ they had to see if they could be eaten.

7. Because there was no dust in the atmosphere, it felt _____ just to breathe.

8. It was frightening for the children to realize that the spaceship was flying through the

   _____ .

9. The colonists didn't know much about their _____ ; it was chosen because it was close.

10. One of the adults brought along the special _____ of a hand set for playing chess.

11. The lake looked clear and good, but we obediently drank from the _____ of water from the ship.

12. Father wondered why _____ boulders would be in the valley and not on the plain.

13. The guide said the plant life was _____ and might act like ground glass in their digestive systems.

14. Peter's computer found extraordinarily slow _____ near the lake shore.

15. Father said he planned to be the _____ , the maker for the planet.

The Green Book—Chapters 4–7

Vocabulary: Using just the vocabulary words given below, fill in the blanks with words that would be appropriate within the context of the story.

hankering	scudding	agony	refugees
bemused	rapt	random	malfunction
intense	hostile	hexagonal	crimson
chrysalis	relevant	bunker	

1. We needed a big _____ to store the grain.

2. The drama of the moths was so hushed and _____ that anyone would have known it was special.

3. Peter originally thought the slow biorhythms must have been a computer

   _____ .

4. The candy trees had little _____ droplets oozing from the bark.

5. The pony book was as _____ on Shine as the history of little green men would have been on Earth.

6. Malcolm and the moth people didn't seem _____ , and wouldn't be a competing life form.

7. The biorhythm reading was really from the sleep rhythms of the moths in _____ stage.

8. Somewhere over the lake, the moths broke line and flew on in _____ scattering.

9. Father was _____ by Patty's enthusiasm on her new planet.

10. The grain looked like _____ yellow beads, shining like golden glass.

11. Father was afraid the grain would cause a death of terrible _____ if they ate it.

12. The Guide advised Father to stop _____ after books.

13. We had come like _____ from far away; we wanted to feel that Shine was our home.

14. The great _____ fluttering crowd of moth people was a silent drama.

15. After the moth people were gone, we missed their _____ shadows.

Short Essay: Write a complete paragraph to answer the following questions.

What will be Father's role on the planet? How does that differ from that of most of the people? What contribution could *you* make to a new civilization?

Name: _____   Date: _____

Final Test
The Green Book

Crossword Puzzle: Use your knowledge of events throughout the book to complete the puzzle.

Down Clues

1. If the planet didn't sustain life the colonists would have to take the _____ .

3. Father exchanged all the _____ they had to borrow *Homer*.

4. Everyone had at least _____ birthdays before they got to Shine.

6. Joe set up a post with holes and pegs to use as a _____ .

7. _____ made a powder from the grain and then made a pancake.

8. The colonists made lamps using _____ .

11. Peter's choice of a luxury had been a little _____ game set.

14. Chickens and _____ were the only livestock they could bring.

Across Clues

2. Father made thread using the moth _____ .

5. The book Joe selected to bring was entitled _____ _____ .

9. The leaves on the trees on Shine were not green but _____ .

10. Father wished he could have also taken his _____ book.

11. Pattie made friends with the moths by giving them tree _____ .

12. _____ named the planet Shine.

13. Joe reminded them that in space there is no _____ .

15. Father read to them aloud from the book of _____ Fairy Tales.

Answer Key

The Green Book *(Worksheet, Chapters 1–3)*

Vocabulary

1. amphitheater	4. diminish	7. invigorating	10. luxury	13. crystalline
2. symmetrical	5. intermediate	8. void	11. flagons	14. biorhythms
3. ointment	6. unpalatable	9. destination	12. glacial	15. contriver

The Green Book *(Worksheet, Chapters 4–7)*

Vocabulary

1. bunker	4. crimson	7. chrysalis	10. hexagonal	13. refugees
2. intense	5. relevant	8. random	11. agony	14. rapt
3. malfunction	6. hostile	9. bemused	12. hankering	15. scudding

Short Essay (Answers will vary.)

Father's role will be to work out inventions, which he considered would be his greatest contribution to the new civilization. Unlike most people, he would not be reproducing anymore. He felt bad about this because reproducing is an essential part of starting a new civilization.

Final Test

Crossword Puzzle

Word List
(for optional use with students)

candy	pills
calendar	rabbits
chess	red
four	Robinson Crusoe
gravity	Sarah
Grimm's	Shakespeare
jellyfish	sugar
Pattie	wings

Extension Activities

The Green Book

Discussion

CHAPTER 1

1. How does Father feel about books? Why doesn't he pick the children's books for them?

2. What are the pills for?

CHAPTER 2

1. The Guide said they were a handpicked group. What did he mean?

2. Why were the colonists so cautious at first?

CHAPTER 3

1. What contributions does Father want to make to the group? Why?

2. Describe Boulder Valley.

CHAPTER 4

1. After the wheat was planted, a bad time began. What things made this a bad time for the colonists?

2. What important discovery did the children make?

CHAPTER 5

1. Describe the moth people.

2. What did the colonists do for the moth people?

CHAPTER 6

1. What makes Father think it will be a long time before the moth people come again?

2. What was Father prepared to do if the bread hurt the children?

CHAPTER 7

1. How important will Pattie's book become to future generations on Shine?

Reading

1. Students who enjoyed this book may enjoy these other books written by the author:

   Fireweed
   Goldengrove
   The Emperor's Winding Sheet
   The Huffler
   Unleaving
   Children of the Fox
   A Chance Child
   A Parcel of Patterns
   Gaffer Samson's Luck

(continued)

2. Many other fantasy books have been written for young adults. Students may enjoy reading:

   **A Wrinkle in Time* by Madeleine L'Engle
   A Swiftly Tilting Planet by Madeleine L'Engle
   A Wind in the Door by Madeleine L'Engle
   The Earthsea Trilogy by Ursula K. LeGuin
   Dragonsong by Anne McCaffrey
   Dragonsinger by Anne McCaffrey
   Dragondrum by Anne McCaffrey

   * covered in Volume III of this series

Writing

1. Write an epilogue for this book. Imagine it is two thousand years later and Pattie's book is still read by the descendants of the colonists. Do the descendants view the book as fact or fiction? Are the moth people extinct or bonded with the human society?

2. Write poems concerning the short life span of the moth people.

Art

1. Illustrate the moth people, the spaceship, or the planet.

2. Make clay models of the moth people.

Video

Although there is no movie of *The Green Book,* there is a movie to accompany the science fiction classic *The Martian Chronicles* by Ray Bradbury. The three-part made-for-TV miniseries is 314 minutes long and follows the lives of Earth people as they colonize the planet Mars.

Into the Dream

by William Sleator

Synopsis

Paul keeps having strange dreams. He sees a small boy running toward . . . something . . . something dangerous? He feels as though he should know the answer. At school, one of the girls in Paul's class, Francine, solves some of the mystery when she explains to Paul, "You're in *my* dream!" And indeed, they are having the same dream and they are both involved in the danger somehow. Together, they try to work out the mystery that includes aliens, mental telepathy, and an amazing dog named Cookie.

Vocabulary

CHAPTER 1
1. vivid
2. relentless
3. urgency
4. speculative
5. "schizo"
6. hostile
7. contempt

CHAPTER 2
1. improbable
2. acutely
3. gamboled
4. oblivious
5. brusque

CHAPTER 3
1. elation
2. petulantly
3. ominous
4. anguish
5. antipathy
6. eerie

CHAPTER 4
1. incompetent
2. radiating

CHAPTER 5
1. conviction
2. chortled

CHAPTER 6
1. psychokinesis
2. menace
3. apprehensively

CHAPTER 7
1. immobilized

CHAPTER 8
1. ramshackle
2. glee
3. foreboding

CHAPTER 9
1. delirious
2. plummeted
3. ascent

CHAPTER 10
1. apparatus
2. emitting

Name: _____ Date: _____

Into the Dream—Chapters 1-5

Vocabulary: Fill in the blanks with appropriate vocabulary words taken from the list below.

gamboled   urgency   vivid
"schizo"   oblivious   antipathy
improbable   radiating   chortled
speculative

1. The dream was a very _____ one.

2. It seemed _____ to Paul that anyone else could have the same dream.

3. The child in the dream _____ across the field toward the light.

4. Larry told Paul that maybe he was becoming _____ .

5. There was a sense of _____ about the dream, as if Paul had to do something soon about it.

6. The child seemed _____ to any danger around him.

7. Paul's _____ toward Francine was changing now that he realized what they had in common.

8. The light in his dream seemed to be _____ out from somewhere.

9. His friend looked at him with a _____ gaze.

10. Delighted to have visitors, Noah _____ with glee.

Short Answer: Using a word or phrase, answer the following questions.

1. What is the first word that Paul hears in the dream? _____

2. At the beginning, what were at least three items that were always in the dream?

   _____

3. What nickname does Francine give to Paul? _____

4. What have Francine and Paul figured out that they both possess?

   _____

5. What does the word "Stardust" represent in reality?

   _____

6. Why was Paul in Nevada for six weeks?

   _____

7. Who was Rose? _____

8. How did they convince Mrs. Jaleela to first talk with them?

   _____

Into the Dream—Chapters 6–10

Synonyms: Match each of the following vocabulary words with a word that has the same or a similar meaning. Write the word in the blank beside its synonym.

glee   apparatus   ascent
menace   plummeted   apprehensively

1. happiness _____

2. fearfully _____

3. fell _____

4. danger _____

5. equipment _____

6. climb _____

Character Identification: Write the character's letter in the blank next to each description of that character. You may use some letters more than once.

(a) Paul   (c) Noah   (e) Mrs. Jaleela

(b) Francine   (d) Cookie

1. _____ Her mother was named Rose.

2. _____ She walked out with her dog to view the bright light.

3. _____ He is four years old.

4. _____ He begins having the dream at the beginning of the book.

5. _____ He leads the children out the window and down the fire escape.

6. _____ She complains of headaches and being sick all the time.

7. _____ Even though he should be able to, he doesn't speak or seem to hear.

8. _____ Goes for an unusual carnival ride with Noah.

9. _____ Very uncomfortable around flashing cameras.

10. _____ She changed from being just a "giggling girl" to being Paul's close friend.

Short Essay: Write complete sentences to answer each of the following questions.

1. What do you think the two men would have done with Noah if they had caught him?

2. Explain how the dream predicted the events that happened at the very end of the book.

Name: _____ Date: _____

Final Test
Into the Dream

Quotations: Identify the character who said each of the following quotes in the book.

1. _____ "I swear, for somebody who's good in school, it sure takes you a while sometimes."

2. _____ "What I won't forget is the name of the motel where we stayed."

3. _____ "Somehow I was drawn to the light but Rose was very hesitant."

4. _____ "He's a national resource, it's true, but now it's too late for anyone to use him as a secret weapon."

5. _____ "It's probably silly of me, but I do feel threatened somehow."

Short Identification: Briefly identify the following:

1. Rose

2. Wonderland

3. Stardust

4. psychokinesis

5. Ms. Keck

Short Essay: Answer the following questions in complete sentences.

1. What is Paul and Francine's theory about the UFO and ESP?

2. What kind of friendship will Paul and Francine have in the future?

Answer Key

Into the Dream (Worksheet, Chapters 1–5)

Vocabulary

1. vivid	3. gamboled	5. urgency	7. antipathy	9. speculative
2. improbable	4. "schizo"	6. oblivious	8. radiating	10. chortled

Short Answer

1. Jaleela
2. the small figure in white, the hulk behind the figure, "Stardust," a low building, light radiating from something
3. Brain Boy
4. ESP or telepathy of some kind
5. a motel in Nevada
6. His parents were getting a divorce.
7. Cookie's mother
8. They said they were working on a school project on UFO's.

Into the Dream (Worksheet, Chapters 6–10)

Synonyms

1. glee
2. apprehensively
3. plummeted
4. menace
5. apparatus
6. ascent

Character Identification

1. d	6. e
2. e	7. c
3. c	8. a
4. a	9. d
5. c	10. b

Short Essay (Answers will vary.)

1. Paul and Francine thought the two men would have used Noah for evil purposes. They could only guess what those purposes would be, but most likely for illegal means.
2. At the end Noah was running toward the amusement park (lights in the dream) with Cookie following closely behind (dark hulk following the child). Noah was dressed in his pajamas (child was clad in white) and the ferris wheel was the ball of light.

Final Test

Quotations

1. Francine
2. Paul's mother
3. Mrs. Jaleela
4. the newsman
5. Mrs. Jaleela

Short Identification

1. Cookie's mother; Mrs. Jaleela's dog.
2. Amusement park at end of book.
3. Name of Nevada motel where Mrs. Jaleela, Paul, and Francine all stayed when the UFO made contact.
4. Ability to move objects without physical contact. Noah has it.
5. Paul and Francine's teacher at school.

Short Essay (Answers will vary.)

1. Paul and Francine believe that the UFO radiated some kind of ESP to the "developing" animals, Noah in utero, Cookie in utero, and also the young children at the time: Paul and Francine. Mrs. Jaleela picked up more than other humans because she went out to view the UFO.
2. They will probably continue their friendship as long as they still have their ESP in common. In fact, this psychic ability may keep them "bonded" even if they choose not to be.

Extension Activities

Into the Dream

Discussion

CHAPTER 1

1. Why is Paul's dream somewhat scary?
2. Why doesn't Paul want to tell his mother about his dream?

CHAPTER 2

1. What new things about the dream does Francine tell Paul?
2. What new things about the little boy in the dream has Paul learned now?

CHAPTER 3

1. Before they find the little child, what do they have to figure out?
2. What does the word "Stardust" represent?

CHAPTER 4

1. Why is the dream getting "so . . . bad"?
2. What facts do they discover in their newspaper research?

CHAPTER 5

1. How does Mrs. Jaleela explain the strange things that happen all the time?
2. What kind of new information do they discover from Mrs. Jaleela?

CHAPTER 6

1. What have they figured out about Cookie? What special powers does she have?
2. What could happen if the wrong kind of people got hold of Noah?

CHAPTER 7

1. Why will Noah only be safe if "the whole world knows about him"?
2. How does Paul's mother seem to also have some kind of ESP?

CHAPTER 8

1. According to Noah, why is it wonderful for him to be with Paul and Francine?
2. How has the dream come true at this point?

CHAPTER 9

1. Why did Noah make the ferris-wheel car fly?
2. Why was Noah's flight good for him?

CHAPTER 10

1. What has finally relieved Mrs. Jaleela's mind?
2. Why is Cookie still a little peeved with Paul and Francine?

(continued)

Reading

1. William Sleator has written many wonderful fantasy and science fiction books. Here is a list of some of those books:

   Singularity
   The Boy Who Reversed Himself
   Strange Attractors
   * *Interstellar Pig*
   Fingers
   Among the Dolls

   * covered in Volume III of this series

2. There are other young adult books that deal specifically with ESP abilities. Some of the best are *The Third Eye* (covered in Volume III of this series) and *A Gift of Magic*, both by Lois Duncan. A young adult book that deals with aliens taking over is *Strange Things Happen in the Woods* (also titled *The Cloverdale Switch*) written by Eve Bunting.

3. There are interesting resource books that deal with all of the topics used in the book. An excellent source is *The People's Almanac* by David Wallechinsky and Irving Wallace. There are short articles on psychic phenomena, ESP, psychokinesis, and mysterious occurrences.

Writing

1. Have students research and write reports on some of the areas discussed in the book: telekinesis, telepathy, ESP, UFO's. Before writing, students should discuss questions such as "Is there scientific proof to substantiate these ideas?" and "Does there have to be scientific proof for something to be believable?"

2. Have students write about a particular dream they remembered vividly.

Art

1. Have students illustrate the dreams, starting out with the first dream and progressing through other drawings with more details.

2. Noah sent out colors with his feelings, such as "there was a flood of orange, with ecstatic blue spirals dancing and sizzling across it" when he was happy. Have students use watercolors to make a color/feeling drawing of the following emotions: hate, fear, love, happiness, excitement. See if the rest of the class can identify the emotions correctly.

The Phantom Tollbooth

by Norton Juster

Synopsis

Milo is a very bored boy. There's nothing to do and he feels that every day is a "waste of time." However, one boring day a play tollbooth appears in his playroom and transports him to a land where nothing is predictable or ordinary. He meets up with interesting companions named Tock and Humbug and together they travel through Dictionopolis and Digitopolis in search of the two sisters, Rhyme and Reason. Along the way Milo discovers the power of words and his own unleashed creativity.

Vocabulary

CHAPTER 1
1. cartographers

CHAPTER 2
1. effusive
2. monotonous
3. doldrums
4. unethical
5. surmise
6. procrastinating
7. conciliatory

CHAPTER 3
1. disrepute
2. battered
3. bunting
4. miscellaneous
5. palatinate
6. connotation
7. reticence

CHAPTER 4
1. minstrels
2. tumult
3. quagmire
4. flabbergast
5. misapprehen-sion
6. disdain
7. adept
8. fraud
9. infuriate

CHAPTER 5
1. havoc
2. dank
3. commendable
4. macabre
5. miserly

CHAPTER 6
1. barren
2. wormwood
3. prosperous
4. flourished
5. grandeur
6. animosity
7. unabridged
8. reconcile
9. arbitration
10. superfluous
11. conveyance

CHAPTER 7
1. famished
2. sonnets

CHAPTER 8
1. repast
2. bouquet
3. distraught
4. regal
5. chasms

6. harrowing
7. perilous
8. prey
9. fiends
10. chaotic
11. crags
12. flattery

CHAPTER 9
1. quest
2. dense
3. promontory

CHAPTER 10
1. luminous
2. mirages
3. illusions
4. profusion
5. gaunt

CHAPTER 11
1. magenta
2. chartreuse
3. dissonance
4. apothecary
5. din
6. pandemonium

CHAPTER 12
1. laudable
2. flourished
3. disconsolate
4. lull
5. crestfallen
6. cascade

CHAPTER 13
1. debris
2. desolate

CHAPTER 14
1. dodecahedron
2. beret
3. grimace
4. stalked
5. eerie
6. stalactites
7. honeycombed
8. intimidated
9. awe

CHAPTER 15
1. caldron
2. savory
3. pungent
4. famine
5. circumference

CHAPTER 16
1. melancholy
2. banished
3. wrath
4. unkempt
5. context
6. cascade
7. crest

CHAPTER 17
1. villainous
2. soothing
3. transfixed
4. plateau
5. crevice
6. fissure

CHAPTER 18
1. precariously
2. ledger
3. verify
4. ovation

CHAPTER 19
1. hindsight
2. malice
3. gorgons
4. dilemma

CHAPTER 20
NONE

The Phantom Tollbooth—Chapters 1–10

Matching: Milo meets many strange people and visits unusual lands. Match up the people, places, or things with their correct definitions. The chapter numbers are given beside the item if you need to use the book.

1. _____ The Whether Man (2)
2. _____ The Doldrums (2)
3. _____ The Lethargarians (2)
4. _____ Tock (2)
5. _____ Dictionopolis (3)
6. _____ The Word Market (3)
7. _____ The Spelling Bee (4)
8. _____ Faintly Macabre, The Official Which (5)
9. _____ Foothills of Confusion (6)
10. _____ Mountains of Ignorance (6)
11. _____ Mathemagician (6)
12. _____ Rhyme and Reason (6)
13. _____ The Castle in the Air (8)
14. _____ King Azaz the Unabridged (7)
15. _____ Humbug (8)
16. _____ Alec (9)
17. _____ Chroma the Great (10)

(a) Home of Rhyme and Reason
(b) The Watchdog
(c) His job is to hurry people past Expectations.
(d) The Ruler of Dictionopolis
(e) Area where words are bought and sold
(f) The Conductor of Color
(g) A long-time prisoner
(h) Insect who loves to spell
(i) Insect who complains about everything
(j) Ruler of Digitopolis
(k) Land surrounding Digitopolis
(l) Land surrounding Dictionopolis
(m) People who want to "get nothing done"
(n) A boy who grows downward
(o) A place where nothing ever happens or changes
(p) Land of words
(q) Rescued by Milo at end of book

Short Essay: Write in complete sentences the answers to the following questions.

1. According to Faintly Macabre, what is the tragedy of the Kingdom of Wisdom?

2. How did Humbug become Milo's "guide" and why did he volunteer to do this job?

Name: _____   Date: _____

The Phantom Tollbooth—Chapters 11–20

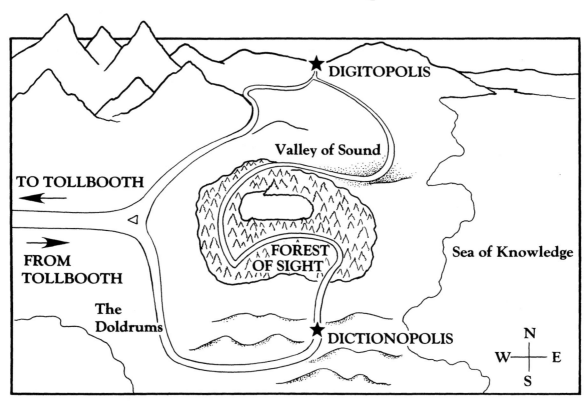

Map Exercise: Place the number of the event on the map where it happened in the book.

1. Place where Milo met Tock.

2. Area where they met Alec.

3. Where the Mathemagician lives.

4. Place where Milo met Humbug.

5. Before Milo came, all sound was abolished here.

Locate and write on the map:

Mountains of Ignorance

Foothills of Confusion

Expectations

Illusions & Reality

Short Essay: Write in complete sentences the answer to the following questions:

1. How did Milo return Rhyme and Reason to the land?

2. What is the Dodecahedron and how does he help Milo?

Name: _____ Date: _____

Final Test
The Phantom Tollbooth

Multiple Response: Choose as many answers as are necessary in order to complete the statement correctly. This means you may choose only one letter, or as many as all four.

1. _____ The place known as Expectations   (a) was the first place Milo traveled to in his car   (b) was ruled by the Mathemagician   (c) is the place you must always go to before you get to where you're going   (d) is where Milo met the Whether Man.

2. _____ In the Market Place of Words   (a) five gentlemen spoke in synonyms   (b) Milo first met Humbug   (c) no sound was permitted   (d) Chroma the Great was conducting the sunrise.

3. _____ Which of the following are all synonyms for "Hello!"?   (a) Greetings   (b) Salutations   (c) Welcome   (d) Farewell

4. _____ Faintly Macabre   (a) is found in the caves of Digitopolis   (b) used to be in charge of choosing words for all occasions   (c) had the official title of "Official Which"   (d) was the sister of Rhyme.

5. _____ King Azaz the Unabridged   (a) was the ruler of the Valley of Sound   (b) was the largest man Milo had ever seen   (c) loved to talk about numbers   (d) had a crown with the alphabet written around it.

6. _____ For the journey to Castle in the Air   (a) Humbug and Tock will accompany Milo   (b) King Azaz gives Milo a box of all the words he will ever need   (c) the Spelling Bee agrees to lead them there   (d) many days of preparation were given to the group before actually departing.

7. _____ Alec says it makes sense to grow downward because   (a) you can kick people more easily   (b) you always have the same viewpoint   (c) you won't fall down so much while growing up   (d) that's the way rain comes to earth.

8. _____ The conductor of the orchestra   (a) was Chroma the Great   (b) was a tall, gaunt man   (c) used a great golden baton to direct   (d) refused to speak to Milo.

9. _____ When Milo visited the Soundkeeper   (a) he found several dogs guarding the place   (b) she told him he could take some sounds as souvenirs   (c) he knew he had to steal just one sound   (d) she refused to let him in.

10. _____ The Dodecahedron   (a) is a five-sided figure   (b) wore a charming beret on top of his head   (c) had twelve faces   (d) knew a great deal about math.

Short Essay: Write a complete paragraph to answer each of the following questions.

1. Choose just one of the characters from the book (besides Milo) and tell why you think he or she would be interesting to meet. Use examples from the book to show why this character was so interesting to you.

2. What do *you* think Milo learned after his journey?

Answer Key

The Phantom Tollbooth (Worksheet, Chapters 1–10)

Matching

1. c	4. b	7. h	10. k	13. a	16. n
2. o	5. p	8. g	11. j	14. d	17. f
3. m	6. e	9. l	12. q	15. i	

Short Essay (Answers will vary.)

1. The two brothers, Azaz and Mathemagician, started arguing about which was better: numbers or words. They put the argument to Rhyme and Reason, who decided they were both equal in importance. The brothers were so enraged by this decision that they banished them from the Kingdom of Wisdom to the Castle in the Air.

2. Humbug told King Azaz exactly what must be done in order to bring Rhyme and Reason back. Everyone was so impressed with Humbug's knowledge of the dangers ahead that they agreed he should be Milo's guide. Humbug really had no desire to do so, but the flattery was so great that he was swept up with it all.

The Phantom Tollbooth (Worksheet, Chapters 11–20)

Map Exercise

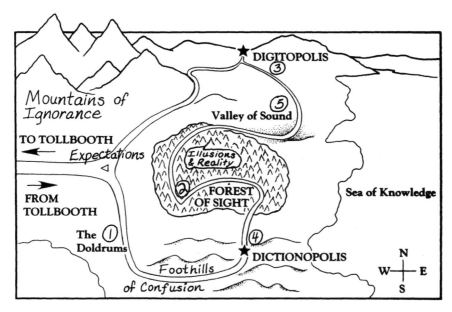

(continued)

Short Essay (Answers will vary.)

1. With horrible creatures coming at them, they all grabbed hold of Tock and flew. As a watchdog, Tock knew that ''time flies'' and therefore, could do this. On land, the group was saved by the armies of Azaz and Mathemagician.

2. The Dodecahedron was built with many lines and angles. He actually had 12 faces but wore a single beret on his head. He was excellent with math and agreed to lead Milo's group to Digitopolis.

Final Test

Multiple Response

1. a, c, d	6. a, b
2. a, b	7. b, c
3. a, b, c	8. a, b
4. b, c	9. c
5. b, d	10. b, c, d

Short Essay

Questions are both opinion questions, so answers will vary.

Extension Activities

The Phantom Tollbooth

Discussion

CHAPTER 1
1. Describe Milo's personality at the beginning of the book.
2. How does he get transported into another world?

CHAPTER 2
1. Why was the Whether Man a "strange man" to Milo?
2. What were the Lethargarians like?
3. Why don't the Lethargarians like Tock?

CHAPTER 3
1. What is ironic about Tock's name?
2. Describe some of the people Milo meets in the Market of Words?

CHAPTER 4
1. What caused the confusion in the Market Place?

CHAPTER 5
1. Why did the policeman arrest Milo and Tock?
2. Describe Faintly Macabre.

CHAPTER 6
1. Retell the story that Faintly Macabre tells.
2. How do Milo and Tock escape from prison?

CHAPTER 7
1. Why does King Azaz think that Milo is just an "ordinary boy"?
2. According to the pastry chefs, what are "half-baked ideas"? Give some examples from the book.

CHAPTER 8
1. What would a person have to do in order to bring Rhyme and Reason back?
2. How did Humbug get designated as guide for the trip?

CHAPTER 9
1. What are the advantages of growing downward, according to Alec?

CHAPTER 10
1. What was unusual about the man who first identified himself as "The Giant"?
2. Why is living in Illusions sometimes easier than living in Reality?
3. What happens at the Evening Concert each night?

CHAPTER 11
1. What very unwise decision did Milo make at the beginning of this chapter?
2. Why is Doctor Dissonance so busy these days?
3. Who is Dynne?

CHAPTER 12
1. What is ironic about the Valley of Sound?
2. How did Milo bring sound back to the valley?

CHAPTER 13
1. How did Milo's group get to the Island of Confusion?

CHAPTER 14
1. Describe the Dodecahedron.

(continued)

2. How does the Dodecahedron help Milo and his friends?

CHAPTER 15

1. How is eating different in Digitopolis?

CHAPTER 16

1. As Milo travels up the stairs to Infinity, who does he meet?

2. What is so frightening about the mountains of Ignorance?

3. What is the name of the "very dirty bird" and what does he do?

CHAPTER 17

1. What bizarre task did the Terrible Trivium have them doing?

2. How did the demon of insincerity help them?

CHAPTER 18

1. What was the duty of the Official Senses Taker?

2. What do you think Milo learned from the Princesses, Rhyme and Reason?

CHAPTER 19

1. What were some of the demons that tried to prevent the Princesses' escape?

2. What solidified the brothers' reign over the Kingdom?

CHAPTER 20

1. When Milo returned to his own home, why was he so excited?

2. How did the whole experience help Milo?

Reading

1. *The Phantom Tollbooth* was written 30 years ago and remains a classic. There are some other books that deal with the main character(s) stepping back into another time. They are:

   For Upper Elementary:

   The Lion, the Witch, and the Wardrobe by C. S. Lewis
   * *The Indian in the Cupboard* by Lynn Reid Banks (and the sequels: *The Return of the Indian* and *The Secret of the Indian*)
   The Castle in the Attic by Elizabeth Winthrop
   Gulliver's Stories Retold by Dolch, Dolch, and Jackson

   For Middle School/Junior High:

   Letters From Atlantis by Robert Silverberg
   The Doll in the Garden by Mary Downing Hahn
   Something Upstairs by Avi
   The Reluctant God by Pamela F. Service
   Vision Quest by Pamela F. Service
   Alice in Wonderland by Lewis Carroll

   * covered in this volume

2. Read aloud to the class the children's book *A Chocolate Moose for Dinner* by Fred Gwynne. The book contains examples of word plays and puns. Have the class come up with their own, maybe figures of speech that they misunderstood when they were younger, and encourage illustrations to match the sayings.

(continued)

The Phantom Tollbooth (continued)

Writing

1. Study homonyms as a class and have students create several of their own homonym creatures similar to those in the book (The Official Which, Dynne, and the Whether Man). Students should write a paragraph about their new character, assuming that Milo is going to meet him or her along his journeys. Have them write in conversational form, explaining the name through the conversation.

2. Write an alternate ending to the book. For example, assume that Milo *did* return the next day. What would he have found? Or, assume that the phantom tollbooth takes Milo to a different realm. Describe this different kingdom.

3. Take just one character in the book and write a complete character sketch of him or her. Describe looks, actions, oddities, etc.

Art

1. Draw an extensive map (using the one in the front of the book as a beginning point, if necessary) of the Kingdom of Wisdom. Color and display the map for the rest of the class.

2. Illustrate some of the scenes from the book that had no illustrations.

3. Using watercolors, paint a picture of what sunset would have been like with Chroma the Great directing. Then paint a picture of what sunrise would have looked like with Milo directing.

Research

Since a knowledge of language and figures of speech is necessary to understand this book, have students complete one of the following projects, either before, during, or after reading the book.

(a) Study figures of speech such as alliteration, irony, and puns. Give examples from the book of each type.

(b) Etymology is the study of the origins of words. Using a dictionary of word origins, find the interesting origins of these words: *realm, king, island, havoc, macabre, pandemonium, pungent, unkempt, villain, gorgons.* Report your findings to the class or create a word origin booklet to share with the class.

(c) In Chapter 16, Milo meets half a boy, or more precisely, a .58 child. He says he's just part of an average family. Research some averages that would relate to your class and draw them in chart form. (Some examples might be the size of an average family, average family income, average number of pets per family.) Use an almanac and other such fact books.

(continued)

Drama

1. Rewrite in play form parts of Chapters 3, 4, and 5, starting with Milo's arrival at the Word Market and continuing until Milo and Tock are taken away to prison. Then use your script to act out the confusion in the Word Market.

2. Write a Reader's Theatre of Chapters 5, 6, and 7. Begin with Milo's introduction to Faintly Macabre and end with the banquet. Present the Reader's Theatre to another class. Be sure to have sufficient introductions written into the piece so anyone could understand what is happening.

Tuck Everlasting

by Natalie Babbitt

Synopsis

The Tuck family looks like an ordinary family to 10-year-old Winnie when she first meets them. But, unbeknownst to her, Winnie has stumbled onto their secret—they have eternal youth. As the Tucks try to explain to young Winnie why this secret must be kept among themselves, Winnie begins to understand many things about life . . . and death. The question Winnie must ask herself takes many years, and much soul-searching, to answer.

Vocabulary

CHAPTERS 1–2

1. tangent
2. tranquil
3. bovine
4. meager
5. oppressive
6. gallows
7. accessible
8. immense
9. melancholy

CHAPTERS 3–4

1. stationary
2. grimace
3. retorted
4. self-deprecation
5. remnants

CHAPTERS 5–6

1. venture
2. amber
3. burly
4. perversely

CHAPTERS 7–8

1. scornful
2. parson
3. elated

CHAPTERS 9–10

1. vanity
2. submission
3. indomitable
4. perilous
5. mirage
6. disarray

CHAPTERS 11–12

1. elation
2. savior
3. luxurious
4. silhouette
5. anguish

CHAPTERS 13–14

NONE

CHAPTERS 15–16

1. barbarian
2. illiterate
3. ordeal
4. constable

CHAPTERS 17–18

1. peril
2. searing
3. alien

CHAPTERS 19–20

1. metaphysics
2. legend
3. immense
4. petulance
5. ghastly
6. marionette
7. envious
8. entranced

CHAPTERS 21–22

1. mingled
2. exertion
3. gingerly

CHAPTERS 23–24

1. ponderous
2. remorseless
3. plaintive
4. parlor
5. lapse
6. gentility
7. prostrate
8. receded
9. ebbed
10. exultant

CHAPTER 25 & EPILOGUE

1. unwittingly
2. constricted
3. apprehensive
4. accomplice
5. wistful
6. prissy
7. revulsion

Name: _____   Date: _____

Tuck Everlasting—Chapters 1-12

Character Identification: Write the character's letter in the blank beside each description of that character. You may use a letter more than once.

(a) Winnie   (b) Angus Tuck   (c) Mae Tuck   (d) Miles Tuck   (e) Jesse Tuck

1. _____ Mother of Jesse and Miles.
2. _____ First meets Jesse by the spring.
3. _____ The older of the two brothers.
4. _____ Walks many miles to meet her boys.
5. _____ Has a music box.
6. _____ Looks like he's 17 or 18 years old.
7. _____ Quite fond of a frog that comes to her yard.
8. _____ Puts Winnie on a horse and "kidnaps" her.
9. _____ Takes Winnie for a ride in a rowboat.
10. _____ Only 10 years old.

Quotations: Write the name of the character who said the following:

1. _____ "Well, boys. Here it is. The worst is happening at last."
2. _____ "Believe me, Winnie Foster, it would be terrible for you if you drank any of this water. I can't let you."
3. _____ "We just are, we just be, like rocks beside the road."
4. _____ "The boys don't be home very much."
5. _____ "Did you hear that? That's the elf music I told you about."
6. _____ "I'm one hundred and four years old."
7. _____ "Please child . . . dear, dear child . . . don't you be scared."
8. _____ "My wife, she finally made up her mind I'd sold my soul to the Devil. She left me."
9. _____ "It pains me to think how your ma and pa will worry, but there's just no way around it."
10. _____ "Well then, seeing you know, I'll go on and say this is the finest thing that's happened in—oh—at least eighty years."

Short Essay: Write a complete paragraph to answer the following question.

Who do you think the man in the yellow suit is and what does he want?

Tuck Everlasting—Chapter 13-Epilogue

Multiple Choice: Choose the one best answer that completes each of the following. Write the letter of your choice in the blank.

1. _____ Mae hit the man in the yellow suit with a (a) hammer (b) lamp (c) shotgun (d) rock.

2. _____ Mae was going to be put on trial for (a) murder (b) kidnapping (c) assault (d) disturbing the peace.

3. _____ The sheriff tells Winnie that if she were older she would be guilty of (a) murder (b) running away from home (c) being an accomplice (d) trespassing.

4. _____ The one present Jesse gave Winnie was (a) the music box (b) a camera (c) a special memory book (d) a bottle of special water.

5. _____ In order for Mae's escape to work, (a) Winnie told the sheriff he had to come quickly to her house (b) they had to drug the sheriff (c) Winnie took Mae's place in the cell (d) they had to use the horses to pull the bars of the cell free.

6. _____ Winnie poured water all over the toad to (a) cool it off (b) protect it from a dog (c) drown it (d) see if it worked.

7. _____ After Mae's escape from the jail, the Tucks were gone from Treegap for about (a) 10 years (b) 20 years (c) 60 years (d) 200 years.

8. _____ When the Tucks returned to Treegap they learned that (a) Winnie had waited for them (b) Jesse and Winnie had married (c) Winnie had died young (d) Winnie had married and died an old woman.

9. _____ One piece of information that pleases the Tucks is that (a) Jesse has married (b) Miles has remarried (c) the woods have been completely torn down (d) everyone in town knows their secret and doesn't care.

10. _____ At the end, the Tucks are certain that (a) the man in the yellow suit never found the secret spring (b) Jesse has died (c) Winnie passed the secret on to her children (d) their old house is still standing.

Synonyms: Match up each of the following vocabulary words with a word that has a similar meaning. Write the word in the blank beside its synonym.

| ebbed | marionette | revulsion | accomplice | constricted |
| mingled | apprehensive | alien | peril | gingerly |

1. fearful: _____

2. strange: _____

3. helper: _____

4. receded: _____

5. mixed: _____

6. puppet: _____

7. disgust: _____

8. carefully: _____

9. danger: _____

10. tightened: _____

Name: _____ Date: _____

Final Test
Tuck Everlasting

Comprehension: Fill in the blanks with nouns (people, places, things) from the book that would make sense in the context of the book.

Winnie was only 10 years old when she first met (1)_____ in the woods. Soon, however, she met the entire (2)_____ family. It was Mae's (3)_____ which calmed Winnie down enough to listen to them. The story they told was unbelievable: There was a (4)_____ that was in the woods outside the town of (5)_____ . The whole family drank from the spring one day, all except the (6)_____ , and they all continued to live, even through accidents and illnesses. (7)_____ even tried to shoot himself to see if he was invincible and indeed, he was.

When (8)_____ went home with the (9)_____ she was scared at first, but after a while she realized how kind they were. (10)_____ took her for a ride in the (11)_____ so he could explain everything to her. (12)_____ even asked her to drink the (13)_____ when she was 17 and then they could get married.

Everything was somewhat calm until (14)_____ showed up. And when (15)_____ hit him to stop him from selling the water from the spring, the (16)_____ happened to see it and arrested Mae. One thing was for sure, Mae could never face the (17)_____ because then everyone would know their secret.

Jesse, Miles, and Angus had all planned Mae's (18)_____ , but it was (19)_____ who finally made it all work.

Answer Key

Tuck Everlasting (*Worksheet, Chapters 1–12*)

Character Identification

1. c	6. e
2. a	7. a
3. d	8. c
4. c	9. b
5. c	10. a

Quotations

1. Mae	6. Jesse
2. Jesse	7. Mae
3. Tuck (Angus)	8. Miles
4. Mae	9. Mae
5. Winnie's grandmother	10. Tuck (Angus)

Short Essay (Answers will vary.)

Since this is a prediction question answers will vary greatly. Some probable ideas: The man is an old friend of the Tucks, a relative, someone hunting for the secret of the Tucks. He wants to warn the Tucks, to find the secret spring, to reunite with the Tucks.

Tuck Everlasting (*Worksheet, Chapters 13–Epilogue*)

Multiple Choice

1. c	6. b
2. a	7. c
3. c	8. d
4. d	9. c
5. c	10. a

Synonyms

1. apprehensive	6. marionette
2. alien	7. revulsion
3. accomplice	8. gingerly
4. ebbed	9. peril
5. mingled	10. constricted

Final Test

Comprehension

1. Jesse	9. Tucks	15. Mae
2. Tuck	10. Tuck (Angus)	16. constable (sheriff)
3. music box	11. rowboat	17. gallows
4. spring (stream)	12. Jesse	18. escape
5. Treegap	13. water	19. Winnie
6. cat	14. the man in the yellow suit (the strange man, the stranger)	
7. Tuck (Angus)		
8. Winnie		

Extension Activities

Tuck Everlasting

Discussion

CHAPTERS 1–2

1. What is strange about the woods around the town of Treegap?
2. What is unusual about the Tuck family?

CHAPTERS 3–4

1. What is Winnie depressed about?
2. What is the "elf music" that so excites Winnie's grandmother?

CHAPTERS 5–6

1. Why didn't Winnie yell as Mae and the boys took her away into the woods?

CHAPTERS 7–8

1. Paraphrase the story the Tucks tell to Winnie.
2. Why do they all feel good at the end of Chapter 8?

CHAPTERS 9–10

1. What are Winnie's impressions of Angus Tuck?
2. How are the Tucks a "family" even though they may not see each other for ten years?

CHAPTERS 11–12

1. Why does Tuck want to talk to Winnie on the pond? Was the place a good choice? Why or why not?

CHAPTERS 13–14

1. What does Tuck have a "bad" feeling about?
2. What unusual proposition does Jesse make to Winnie at this time?

CHAPTERS 15–16

1. Why does the man in the yellow suit seem less than trustworthy?
2. What is surprising about the Fosters selling the woods?

CHAPTERS 17–18

1. What does Winnie discover from her fishing trip with Miles?
2. Why do you think Winnie thinks of Tuck as the "dearest of them all"?

CHAPTERS 19–20

1. What scheme does the man with the yellow suit have?
2. What has happened that puts the future of the spring in jeopardy?

CHAPTERS 21–22

1. Why did Mae have to kill the man in the yellow suit?
2. What is their escape plan?

CHAPTERS 23–24

1. What would be advantageous if Winnie later married Jesse?
2. How will this second adventure change her parents' trust of her?

CHAPTER 25 & EPILOGUE

1. How did this last adventure change Winnie's reputation?
2. Why did Winnie help the frog in the way she did?
3. In the end, did Winnie make a good choice? Why or why not?

(continued)

Tuck Everlasting (continued)

Reading

1. Searching for the Fountain of Youth is not an unusual concept. Students might want to read about the Spanish explorer Ponce de Leon, who tried to find the fountain of youth in the territory we know today as Florida.

2. A young adult mystery that deals with eternal youth (not eternal life such as in *Tuck Everlasting*) is *Locked in Time* by Lois Duncan.

3. Other books by Natalie Babbitt include the following:

   The Devil's Storybook
   The Eyes of the Amaryllis
   Goody Hall
   Kneeknock Rise
   Phoebe's Revolt
   The Search for Delicious

Writing

1. Have each student "become" one of the Tucks and write his or her observations of the following events: the Civil War, World War II, the atomic bomb, automobiles. Remind the students to stay in character and write only how they feel their characters would feel about these developments.

2. Place the Tucks in this current year. Have students answer the following questions as one of the characters in the Tuck family.

   (a) What do you think is the greatest achievement that has been made in the past 200 years?

   (b) What do you think is the worst change in society in the past 200 years?

   (c) What has been your best memory?

3. If Winnie could have written to Jesse explaining why she was not going to marry him, what would she have said? Have students write this imaginary letter to Jesse, explaining her reasons for her decision.

Drama

Have students role-play the scene that would have happened if Jesse had returned to talk Winnie out of her wedding.

HISTORICAL NOVELS

Cave Under the City

by Harry Mazer

Synopsis

In the Depression of the 1930's 12-year-old Tolley becomes the sole person responsible for his younger brother, when his father is far away trying to find work and his mother is hospitalized. First, Tolley figures they can hide out in their apartment, but when the authorities come looking for them, a new location must be found. An abandoned, burned-out restaurant becomes their "cave under the city," and they learn to survive on the streets of New York City almost any way they can.

Vocabulary

CHAPTERS 1–2

1. ace
2. cannibal
3. delicatessen
4. grotto

CHAPTERS 3–4

1. sweatshop
2. marrow
3. eviction
4. dumbwaiter

CHAPTERS 5–6

1. suave
2. capitalism
3. egotistical
4. pneumonia
5. carcasses

CHAPTERS 7–8

1. ointment
2. botanical
3. pulmonary
4. ward

CHAPTERS 9–10

1. alcove

CHAPTERS 11–12

1. awnings

CHAPTERS 13–14

1. pester

CHAPTERS 15–16

1. aggravate

CHAPTERS 17–18

1. stingy
2. mangy

CHAPTERS 19–20

1. resign
2. salmon

CHAPTERS 21–22

1. satchel

CHAPTERS 23–24

1. cardigan
2. glinting
3. khaki
4. charity

CHAPTERS 25–26

NONE

CHAPTERS 27–28

1. aviator
2. vendor
3. gnawed

CHAPTERS 29–30

1. gargoyles
2. hassock

CHAPTERS 31–32

1. burrowed
2. sanatorium

CHAPTER 33

1. renovating
2. scaffolding

REFERENCES TO THE 1930's*

1. Lou Gehrig
2. Lindbergh kidnapping
3. Bruno Hauptmann
4. Sacco & Vanzetti
5. President Roosevelt
6. Errol Flynn
7. *The Shadow*

*Information on these is given in the Extension Activities.

Name: _____ Date: _____

Cave Under the City—Chapters 1–13

Vocabulary: Using just the vocabulary list below, fill in the blanks with the appropriate words.

delicatessen   pulmonary   carcasses
eviction   dumbwaiter

1. Tolley ran to the _____ to get some meat.

2. His mother was put in the _____ ward of the hospital.

3. He knew what _____ meant; all too often his neighbors were being thrown out of their homes.

4. The _____ in their apartment would bring up the block of ice from the iceman.

5. The _____ hung in view of the customers in the butcher's shop.

Short Answer: Answer, with a word or a name, the following questions. All are based on historical information of the 1930's given in the book.

1. Name one of the presidents of the United States during the Depression. _____

2. Finish this famous quote of the time: "We have nothing to fear but _____ ."

3. Name a popular radio show mentioned in the book. _____

4. Name a popular movie star of the 1930's who was mentioned in the book. _____

Essay: Answer the following in at least one or two complete paragraphs.

Describe what life in the 1930's was like, according to the book. Be sure to include differences in today's world.

Cave Under the City—Chapters 14–33

Sequencing: Number from 1 to 8 in the correct order in which these events occurred in the book.

_____ Tolley's father first leaves to find work south of New York.

_____ Tolley's father takes his sons to the cafeteria and tells them not to worry about price.

_____ Tolley's mother is taken to the hospital.

_____ Their father returns to find his sons abandoned.

_____ Tolley and Bubber create their own home in a burned-out restaurant.

_____ King runs off, never to return.

_____ Whitey helps them get more for their tires.

_____ Tolley and Bubber visit their mother in a sanatorium.

Matching: Match up the vocabulary words with their correct meanings. Write the letter of the meaning in the blank beside the word.

1. _____ vendor
2. _____ aviator
3. _____ stingy
4. _____ salmon
5. _____ resign
6. _____ cardigan
7. _____ khaki
8. _____ charity
9. _____ aggravate
10. _____ burrowed
11. _____ renovating
12. _____ satchel
13. _____ hassock
14. _____ mangy
15. _____ sanatorium

(a) A type of fish

(b) The act of giving

(c) Bother

(d) Seller

(e) Type of sweater

(f) Brownish-green fabric

(g) Crawled down and buried into

(h) Give up

(i) Greedy

(j) Pilot

(k) Firmly stuffed cushion

(l) Filthy and shabby

(m) Hospital for rest

(n) Rebuilding and modernizing

(o) Small suitcase or bag

Name: _____   Date: _____

Final Test
Cave Under the City

Multiple Response: Choose as many answers as are needed in order to complete the statement accurately. This means you may write only one letter in the blank, or as many as all four.

1. _____ The book takes place (a) in New York City (b) during the 1950's (c) during the 1930's (d) during a time of depression for the U.S.

2. _____ Tolley's mother (a) had mental problems (b) was ill (c) was taken to a sanatorium (d) did not know that her children were living on the streets.

3. _____ Tolley's father (a) had been working in Baltimore (b) finally got work in Virginia (c) never got Tolley's letter (d) was an alcoholic.

4. _____ Tolley took care of his little brother by (a) watching over him when he was ill (b) taking him to the children's shelter for food (c) getting food for him (d) finding a dog to watch him while he was gone.

5. _____ Tolley was scared of Mr. McKenzie because (a) Mr. McKenzie might tell his father where Tolley and Bubber were (b) Mr. McKenzie might report him for stealing (c) Tolley and Bubber would have to go to the children's shelter (d) Mr. McKenzie was ready to kill the two children.

6. _____ King (a) was more of Bubber's dog than Tolley's (b) seemed to be a fairly smart dog (c) warned them about the caved-in restaurant (d) ran off at the end.

7. _____ When Tolley returned to school (a) he found out he had missed a whole civics unit (b) he gave a report on his life on the streets (c) the teacher asked him where he had been (d) he was lowered a grade level.

8. _____ Tolley is ashamed that (a) he stole from the milkman (b) he took two donuts from the grocer (c) they had to live in the ruins of a building (d) his father couldn't find a job.

9. _____ Tolley's grandmother (a) was sick also (b) told the children to go to the children's shelter (c) lived in Maryland (d) gave the children some money.

10. _____ In the end, (a) King had left (b) Tolley's mother was still sick (c) Tolley's grandmother was sick (d) Tolley's father had a job in the city.

Short Essay: Answer the following in a complete paragraph.

What inner resources did Tolley discover within himself? Give examples from the book that show these inner resources.

Answer Key

Cave Under the City *(Worksheet, Chapters 1–13)*

Vocabulary

1. delicatessen
2. pulmonary
3. eviction
4. dumbwaiter
5. carcasses

Short Answer

1. Franklin D. Roosevelt
2. fear itself
3. Possible answers: *The Lone Ranger, Tarzan, The Shadow*
4. Possible answers: Errol Flynn, Clark Gable, Ronald Colman, Jean Harlow, Wallace Beery, Tom Mix, Norma Shearer

Essay (Answers will vary.)

The book described differences between life today and the 1930's in three areas: entertainment, economics, and daily life. Entertainment was much simpler: no VCR's, no TV's, no Walkmans or MTV, no video games. Many people believe that children then were more imaginative and creative because radio and movies provided the opportunity for children to act out further dramas. Baseball was *the* American sport with heroes galore: Babe Ruth, Cy Young, Lou Gehrig, Joe DiMaggio. Movie stars were almost royalty.

Economics and daily life somewhat merge together. Communication was difficult at times and very slow compared to today. In the book, the reader saw how many times mail was never delivered and misunderstandings happened because of poor communication. Many workers were immigrants and because of their lack of English and formal schooling, jobs were limited for them.

Cave Under the City *(Worksheet, Chapters 14–33)*

Sequencing

1, 7, 2, 6, 3, 5, 4, 8

Matching

1. d	3. i	5. h	7. f	9. c	11. n	13. k	15. m
2. j	4. a	6. e	8. b	10. g	12. o	14. l

Final Test

Multiple Response

1. a, c, d
2. b, c, d
3. a, c
4. a, c
5. c
6. a, b, c, d
7. a
8. a, b, c
9. a
10. a, b, c, d

Short Essay (Answers will vary.)

Tolley discovered many things about himself. First, he found out that he could be creative and create a "shelter" out of almost anything. He discovered that no matter how much Bubber exasperated him, he still was responsible and mature enough to protect him. Out of necessity, Tolley became quick and stealthy with his stealing. He also thought up several plans for their survival, which shows his resourcefulness.

Extension Activities

Cave Under the City

Discussion

Historical Notes

There are several historical references that students should be aware of as they read the book. Following is a brief description of some of these events.

- **Lou Gehrig**—One of baseball's all-time greats. He played for the New York Yankees from 1923 to 1939.

- **Lindbergh kidnapping**—Charles Lindbergh was a famous American aviator who made the first nonstop solo flight from New York to Paris in 1927. Four years after this historic flight his firstborn son, Charles, Jr., was kidnapped and found murdered. The child was 20 months old. The case and subsequent trial were headline news for months.

- **Bruno Hauptmann**—The man accused of kidnapping and killing the Lindbergh baby. Although he always claimed his innocence, he was executed.

- **Sacco & Vanzetti**—Two men convicted of killing two men in a robbery in 1927. After seven years in prison and with much public protest, they were executed.

- **Franklin D. Roosevelt**—President from 1933 to 1945; led America through the Depression and World War II.

- **Errol Flynn**—Flamboyant movie star of the 1930's; known for his Robin Hood role and dashing ways.

- *The Shadow*—Famous radio program of the 1930's; based on mysteries and the famous saying "The Shadow knows."

CHAPTERS 1–2
1. Why are times tough for Tolley and his family?
2. What frustrates Tolley? Is he right to get upset over this?

CHAPTERS 3–4
1. Why did Tolley's father leave?
2. How are things changing in Tolley's neighborhood?

CHAPTERS 5–6
1. What has happened to Tolley's mother? Were there signs that could have prepared Tolley for this?
2. What happens when they show up at their grandmother's?

CHAPTERS 7–8
1. What is Tolley's first plan of action?
2. What do you think Social Services would have done for the children?

CHAPTERS 9–10
1. Why is Tolley so frightened of the children's shelter?

CHAPTERS 11–12
1. What does Chapter 11 tell you about Mrs. Chrissman?
2. What living alternative have they found?

CHAPTERS 13–14
1. What's the worst thing you can do when you're hungry, according to Tolley?

(continued)

2. What techniques are they using inside the apartment so no one will know they're there?

CHAPTERS 15–16

1. What are some possible reasons Tolley's father hasn't returned?

2. What is their "cave"? What might go wrong with this hiding place?

CHAPTERS 17–18

1. How have they used a Christmas tree?

2. What decision has Tolley made at the end of Chapter 18? Is it a wise one?

CHAPTERS 19–20

1. How was King "good luck"?

2. How are Tolley and Bubber getting on each other's nerves?

CHAPTERS 21–22

1. What is shaming Tolley now?

2. Is it "wrong" for Tolley to steal food? Explain.

CHAPTERS 23–24

1. What is the one constant in their lives?

2. What is ironic about their visit to the zoo?

3. How did they meet Whitey?

CHAPTERS 25–26

1. What new plan is Tolley coming up with? What are the advantages and disadvantages of this plan?

2. What did Whitey teach them?

CHAPTERS 27–28

1. What do they do now for entertainment?

2. Why is their existence on the streets almost becoming unbearable?

CHAPTERS 29–30

1. How does Bubber act responsibly?

CHAPTERS 31–32

1. What happened to King? Why?

2. What was Tolley's reaction to his father's return?

CHAPTER 33

1. How is Tolley's attitude about life different now?

2. What do you think Bubber will remember about their experiences on the street?

Reading

1. Harry Mazer is a prolific writer for young people. Some of his books are:

City Light	*The War on Villa Street*
I Love You, Stupid!	*The Island Keeper*
* *Snow Bound*	*The Last Mission*
When the Phone Rang	

   * covered in Volume II of this series

2. There are two other books for young people concerning the Depression. The books are *No Promises in the Wind* by Irene Hunt (covered in Volume II of this series) and *The Journey of Natty Gann* by Ann Matthews. The latter was made into a Disney movie and would be an appropriate follow-up to *Cave Under the City*.

(continued)

Writing

1. Tolley thought no one would believe his tale if he wrote about his experiences for school. Have students become Tolley and write this essay about his life on the streets.

2. Have students write an essay on how hunger changes a person, using Tolley's experiences as a guide.

Research

1. This book has many references that students could research and report on. These are some of them:

Lou Gehrig	*The Lone Ranger*	Jean Harlow	*Flash Gordon*
Ronald Colman	*The Shadow*	Clark Gable	*Tarzan*
Errol Flynn	Tom Mix	Wallace Beery	Norma Shearer

2. Have pairs of students research the court cases of Bruno Hauptmann and Sacco & Vanzetti. Then have the teams decide on a position of either guilt or innocence and have them debate their sides.

3. Students should study the Depression from a political and economic viewpoint. How did it start? What did President Roosevelt do to help people get through the Depression? Were any groups of people hit harder than others? What finally brought the nation out of the Depression?

Art

Have students draw a U.S. map based on question 3 in the Research section above. Have them label different areas of extreme drought, poverty, and unemployment, and also label the places of opportunity.

Drama

1. Have students write and act out the scene where Tolley and Bubber get to visit their mother for the first time in the sanatorium.

2. Have students improvise the following scenes:

    (a) A meeting between Whitey and Tolley several days after he "stood" them up.

    (b) Tolley's first day back at school with his old gang asking him questions.

    (c) Tolley and Bubber visiting their grandmother in the hospital.

    (d) Tolley (as a grandfather) telling his grandchildren about his "cave."

    (e) Years later, when the two boys are grown, Bubber and Tolley talking about their experiences on the streets.

177

The Devil's Arithmetic

by Jane Yolen

Synopsis

Thirteen-year-old Hannah reluctantly attends her family's traditional celebration of Passover. Just as she feared, Hannah must listen to the older relatives remembering the Holocaust. Hannah is asked to continue Jewish tradition by opening the door for the prophet Elijah. Instead she finds she has opened the door of history and becomes trapped herself in the horrors of the Holocaust. This masterfully written young adult novel provides painful yet poignant descriptions of the death-camp experience.

Vocabulary

CHAPTER 1

1. Passover
2. Seder
3. unleavened
4. Haggadah

CHAPTER 2

1. concentration camp
2. Yiddish
3. distorted
4. saga
5. compensation

CHAPTER 3

1. exodus
2. yarmulke
3. matzoh
4. kosher
5. rabbi
6. Chanukah
7. Elijah
8. prophet
9. fraud

CHAPTER 4

1. elaborate
2. contagious
3. cascaded
4. conspiratorial
5. simultaneously
6. Torah

CHAPTER 5

1. demonstrate
2. pursue
3. efficiency

CHAPTER 6

1. distinguish
2. plaits
3. fierce
4. ferret
5. privy

CHAPTER 7

1. compression
2. mesmerized
3. appreciative
4. clique
5. abrupt

CHAPTER 8

1. dominant
2. undecipherable
3. lucid

CHAPTER 9

1. persuasive
2. plaintive
3. relocated
4. humanely
5. billeted
6. desecrate
7. reluctant
8. Holocaust
9. crematoria

CHAPTER 10

1. periphery
2. protruding
3. satchel
4. profound
5. persistent
6. stench
7. spontaneously
8. alienates
9. impudent

CHAPTER 11

1. uninflected

CHAPTER 12

1. ingrate
2. dissipating

CHAPTER 13

1. unwarranted
2. arbitrary
3. elusive
4. vivid

CHAPTER 14

1. midden

CHAPTER 15

1. pervasive
2. contorted

CHAPTER 16

1. chaos
2. eroded
3. riveted

CHAPTER 17

1. portents

CHAPTER 18

1. defiantly
2. irony
3. superimposed

CHAPTER 19

1. l'chaim

EPILOGUE

1. remnants

Name: _____ Date: _____

The Devil's Arithmetic—Chapters 1–9

Vocabulary: Fill in the blanks correctly with words taken from the list below.

lucid	exodus	plaits	saga
Holocaust	simultaneously	fraud	privy
dominant	persuasive	mesmerized	fierce
contagious	reluctant	elaborate	

1. Grandpa Will talked on and on about the plagues and the Jewish _____ from Egypt.

2. She kept remembering more things she had learned in history classes about the terrors of the

   _____ .

3. Shmuel said that with their guns aimed, the Germans' orders to relocate were very

   _____ .

4. Gitl said that after the illness Chaya was sometimes _____ , and then sometimes telling crazy tales.

5. Chaya _____ the village girls with her stories.

6. She wove Chaya's hair into _____ which were then pinned on her head like a crown.

7. They climbed into the boxcars in family groups, _____ to be parted.

8. Shmuel was so happy about his bride that his joy seemed _____ to those around him.

9. Hannah was worried that even her mother would start to retell another old family

   _____ .

10. It was like hearing two languages spoken _____ to Hannah, both Yiddish and English.

11. Hannah felt like a _____ being complimented by Grandpa Will on her generosity.

12. She discovered that the cottage's _____ was outside and had no light for night visits.

13. Outside the village the _____ color was brown, like an old photograph.

14. Gitl had a reputation of being _____ like a bear.

15. At first, Hannah thought the cottage and these people were parts of an _____ dream.

Short Answer: On the back of this page or on a separate sheet of paper, answer the following questions in one or two complete sentences.

1. Why don't the villagers believe Chaya when she warns them about the Nazis?

2. Why didn't Hannah want to attend the Passover celebration?

The Devil's Arithmetic—Chapters 10-Epilogue

Vocabulary: Fill in the blanks correctly with words taken from the list below.

periphery	midden	unwarranted	stench
riveted	satchel	dissipating	eroded
superimposed	profound	portents	chaos
defiantly	protruding	contorted	

1. There had been no _____ or clues that the time to attempt escape was close.

2. There were armed guards in front and around the _____ of the station house.

3. Although the rules were insane, without them, there would be _____ .

4. The silence was so _____ that Hannah wondered if she had gone deaf.

5. Her two sets of memories seemed _____ , one on top of the other.

6. The children were hidden from the Commandant in the _____ .

7. Hannah's cheeks burned from the _____ slaps.

8. The _____ in the crowded boxcar was overwhelming.

9. Fayge's wedding dress was caught on a _____ nail.

10. The black smoke from the smokestack was _____ against the blue sky.

11. The guard's face _____ into a mask of anger and hatred.

12. The memories of her other life _____ and disappeared at the camp.

13. Their attention was _____ on the prisoners who were about to be killed.

14. Shmuel stood up straight with his chin thrust out _____ .

15. Fayge was surprised to see her grandmother's tapestry _____ at the station.

Short Answer: Answer the following questions in one or two complete sentences.

1. How does the devil's arithmetic help the prisoners?

2. What eventually happened to Gitl after the war?

Name: _____ Date: _____

Final Test
The Devil's Arithmetic

Sequencing: Number from 1 to 10 in the order in which these events happened in the book.

_____ Fayge is executed with Shmuel.

_____ Rivka explains the devil's arithmetic.

_____ Shmuel is afraid of "getting" married.

_____ The ride in the boxcar.

_____ Hannah opens the door for Elijah.

_____ Shmuel is captured trying to escape.

_____ Chaya tells Rivka to run for her life.

_____ The tattooer recognizes his daughter's dress.

_____ Hannah is allowed to drink wine with the adults.

_____ Hannah tells Aunt Eva that she remembers the past.

True/False: Write *true* or *false* for each of the following statements.

1. _____ Chaya is a Yiddish word meaning "life."

2. _____ Many Jewish villagers escaped into the forests.

3. _____ Chaya saved Rivka's life so she would remember.

4. _____ Gitl was married to a man from America.

5. _____ Hannah and Grandpa Will were very close.

6. _____ The village girls loved Chaya's stories.

7. _____ The badchan chose to die.

8. _____ The blokova had some missing fingers.

9. _____ The Commandant didn't bother to look in the midden.

10. _____ The German sign said "Work makes you free."

Short Essay: Answer the following in a complete paragraph.

Why does Hannah take Rivka's place for "processing"?

Answer Key

The Devil's Arithmetic *(Worksheet, Chapters 1–9)*

Vocabulary

1. exodus
2. Holocaust
3. persuasive
4. lucid
5. mesmerized
6. plaits
7. reluctant
8. contagious
9. saga
10. simultaneously
11. fraud
12. privy
13. dominant
14. fierce
15. elaborate

Short Answer

1. Chaya had recently been very ill and they think she is still somewhat delirious. She is also very young and couldn't know these futuristic things she claims to know.

2. She doesn't like to hear her older relatives talk about the Holocaust.

The Devil's Arithmetic *(Worksheet, Chapters 10–Epilogue)*

Vocabulary

1. portents
2. periphery
3. chaos
4. profound
5. superimposed
6. midden
7. unwarranted
8. stench
9. protruding
10. dissipating
11. contorted
12. eroded
13. riveted
14. defiantly
15. satchel

Short Answer

1. It gives a meaning to each of the numbers tattooed on the prisoners' arms. It helps them to remember each other's numbers, and reminds each prisoner of his or her own individuality.

2. She emigrated to Israel with Yitzchak, neither of whom married. She organized a rescue mission there for survivors of the Holocaust and helped to locate their families. The mission later became an adoption agency called CHAYA, Life.

Final Test

Sequencing

8, 6, 3, 4, 2, 7, 9, 5, 1, 10

True/False

1. true
2. false
3. true
4. false
5. false
6. true
7. true
8. true
9. true
10. true

Short Essay

Hannah had just told the girls that the Jews do have a good future and that they will survive. She wanted Rivka to survive and remember her message to tell the others.

Extension Activities

The Devil's Arithmetic

Discussion

CHAPTER 1

1. What kind of story did Hannah make up for her brother?
2. How did Hannah get her name?

CHAPTER 2

1. How does Hannah feel about Aunt Eva?

CHAPTER 3

1. Why does Hannah's head throb?
2. Why does Hannah get to open the door?
3. What does she see?

CHAPTER 4

1. What does the reader know of Chaya's history?
2. Why does Hannah go along with all this?

CHAPTER 5

1. How do Gitl and Shmuel react when Chaya tells them of her other life?

CHAPTER 6

1. What does Rachel want from Chaya?
2. Why doesn't Hannah tell these people the truth?

CHAPTER 7

1. What is a badchan hired to do?
2. What does the badchan tell Hannah?
3. Why is Hannah so popular with the girls?

CHAPTER 8

1. What does the badchan call the man with the medals?
2. What has Hannah just realized?

CHAPTER 9

1. What do the others think when Chaya tries to tell them about the death camps?
2. Why do the villagers go?
3. What warnings does the badchan give?

CHAPTER 10

1. What was the reaction when Chaya suggested going to Israel? Why?

CHAPTER 11

1. How long were they in the boxcar?
2. What happened to Rachel?
3. Why did Gitl and Chaya promise not to cry?

CHAPTER 12

1. What did the tattooer realize?

CHAPTER 13

1. Why did Gitl hit Chaya?
2. How is Chaya's memory changed?

CHAPTER 14

1. What does Rivka "organize"?
2. How does Chaya help remember the numbers?
3. What are some camp rules?

(continued)

183

CHAPTER 15

1. What happened to the badchan? Why?

CHAPTER 16

1. How did the blokova lose her fingers?

2. What message was Fayge trying to give the others about the soul?

CHAPTER 17

1. How does Gitl describe the change in Fayge?

CHAPTER 18

1. What hope do they have for Yitzchak?

2. Why do you think Chaya took Rivka's place?

CHAPTER 19

1. What event releases Chaya and makes Hannah return?

Reading

1. Other books regarding the Holocaust which may be appropriate for young adult students are:

   The Diary of Anne Frank by Anne Frank
   Anne Frank: Life in Hiding by Johanna Hurwitz
   The Short Life of Sophie Schol by Herman Vinke
   The Upstairs Room by Johanna Reiss
   Fredrich by Hans Peter Richter
   Upon the Head of the Goat by Aranka Siegal
   * *Number the Stars* by Lois Lowry
   The Devil in Vienna by Doris Orgel
   Escape or Die by Ina R. Friedman

   * covered in this volume

2. Jane Yolen has written a wide range of children's books and young adult novels, including science fiction and picture books for younger children. Here are just some of the books she has written:

   Cards of Grief
   Dragonfield and Other Stories
   Dragon's Blood
   The Gift of Sarah Baker
   Heart's Blood
   The Magic Three of Solatia
   Merlin's Booke
   Sleeping Ugly

(continued)

Writing

1. Have three different small groups of committees of students work together to write a play version of these three events in the book:

   (a) The family gathering for Passover, ending with Hannah opening the door for Elijah.

   (b) The wedding procession, ending with the villagers getting into the Nazi trucks.

   (c) The escape attempt, ending with Hannah, Shifre, and Esther walking "into endless night."

2. Based on the information in this book, have students write an essay on what people today should know about the Holocaust.

3. Have students write an essay comparing and contrasting Hannah at the beginning and at the end of the book.

Research

1. Have students research Poland's Nazi occupation.

2. Have students research Auschwitz during the war and today.

3. Have students research the establishment of Israel after World War II.

Drama

1. Have students present (with scripts) the three scenes they created in play version for assignment 1 in the Writing section.

2. Have students read the play version of *The Diary of Anne Frank*.

Video

The movie *The Diary of Anne Frank* would be an excellent closure activity for students who read *The Devil's Arithmetic*.

A Family Apart

by Joan Lowery Nixon

Synopsis

When her oldest son Mike gets into trouble with the law, Mrs. Kelly realizes she cannot be a full-time provider as well as a full-time mother for her six children. Rather than have Mike serve a long prison term, Mrs. Kelly agrees to a deal with the judge. All of her children will be sent west on the Orphan Train to find adoptive families and a better life. Mrs. Kelly looks to her oldest daughter, Frances, for support and understanding, but instead Frances feels deeply betrayed and abandoned. This first in a set of four novels introduces each of the children to their western families and sets the stage for their adventures.

Vocabulary

CHAPTER 1
1. sepia

CHAPTER 2
1. cobbled street
2. dawdled
3. docked
4. shawl
5. brandishing
6. pedestrians
7. precariously
8. pungent
9. pro-slavery
10. pamphlet
11. urchins
12. heedless
13. ornate
13. balustrade
14. curlicues
15. woebegone
16. sentinels
17. pulverized

CHAPTER 3
1. reluctant
2. idolized
3. indignation
4. discarded

CHAPTER 4
1. relate
2. urgency
3. parcel
4. portly
5. accusation
6. ragamuffins
7. circumstances
8. convictions
9. pickpocket

CHAPTER 5
1. destination
2. resistant
3. pantalets
4. reassured
5. abandoned

CHAPTER 6
1. resentment
2. satchel
3. hamper
4. bounty

CHAPTER 7
1. appraising
2. entitled
3. baritone
4. trestles
5. retrieve

CHAPTER 8
1. valise
2. prominent
3. reputation
4. distracted
5. homespun
6. mingled
7. pulpit

CHAPTER 9
1. betrayed
2. valiant
3. rebellious
4. rotund

CHAPTER 10
1. homestead
2. dubious
3. orator
4. abolitionist
5. Underground Railroad
6. dollop
7. utensils
8. pummeled
9. pallets

CHAPTER 11
1. contemptuously
2. rebuked
3. parlor
4. chagrined

CHAPTER 12
1. diphtheria
2. fodder

CHAPTER 13
1. spunk
2. prairie

A *Family Apart*—Chapters 1–6

Vocabulary: Fill in the blanks with words taken from the list below.

pulverized	parcel	docked
ornate	resentment	accusation
satchel	urchins	sepia
pamphlet	destination	bounty
pickpocket	sentinels	idolized

1. Captain Taylor said that when he travels he carries his gun in his _____ .

2. Mr. Brace told the children that their _____ was St. Joseph, Missouri.

3. Ma gave Mr. Brace the paper _____ which contained all her children's belongings.

4. When Da was sick, Ma fed him a mixture of _____ beef bones mixed with red wine.

5. The awful man laughed at Frances and said he knew that street _____ like her couldn't read.

6. "The Life of Abraham Lincoln" was offered as a _____ for 4 cents a copy.

7. Mr. Lomax _____ her pay 10 cents because he said she dawdled.

8. Grandma Briley's book contained a _____ -toned photograph.

9. The Captain explained that _____ hunters profit from hunting down runaway slaves.

10. Ma made Mike give his solemn promise never to be a _____ again.

11. Danny always _____ his older brother.

12. Ma was at work rubbing the brass on the _____ staircase in the office building.

13. Ma often spoke of Ireland's Bens, the mountains that stood like _____ watching over her homeland.

14. Frances felt her love for her mother turn into _____ at being abandoned.

15. The official _____ against Mike was assault and robbery.

Short Answer: Answer in one or two sentences the following question.

The passengers have two different views about bounty hunters. What are they?

A Family Apart—Chapters 7-13

Vocabulary: Fill in the blanks correctly with words taken from the list below.

valise	reputation
dollop	entitled
rebuked	valiant
prominent	parlor
spunk	retrieve
homespun	trestles

1. Frances helped Mrs. Busby as she added a _____ of soap to the dishwater.

2. As Frances sat in the _____ on a stool near his chair, Jake explained the Underground Railroad.

3. Frances felt her best defense against the bounty hunter would be a show of

   _____ .

4. Mr. Crandon said he was _____ to as much peace and quiet as the railroad company could provide.

5. A committee of three _____ citizens approved the applicants.

6. Katherine pulled a small _____ from under the train's seat and began to extract hairbows for the girls.

7. Captain Taylor told Mike that he had not sacrificed his _____ and should build on his future.

8. Mr. Crandon was upset because Mike didn't _____ his gold money clip from the bandit.

9. The train crossed _____ and bridges on its way west.

10. In St. Joseph, the women were dressed in dark _____ .

11. Frances could tell Danny was making a _____ effort and she was proud of him.

12. Petey laughed at the story about a boy _____ by his dog.

Short Answer: Answer the following questions in one or two complete sentences.

1. What does Frances learn about sacrifice from her experience with Janus and Odette?

2. How did Katherine help Frances and the Marshal?

Final Test
A Family Apart

Character Identification: Write the name of the character in the blank next to each description of that character. You may use a name more than once.

Grandma Briley   Mrs. Kelly   Frances
Danny   Mike   Janus and Odette
Megan   Jeff   Captain Taylor
Mr. and Mrs. Cummings Peg   Johnny
Andrew McNair   Katherine   Mr. Crandon

1. _____ Was glad to be friends with Frankie.

2. _____ Lost two sons to diphtheria.

3. _____ Their son was given away as a wedding present.

4. _____ Dressed as a boy in order to keep a promise.

5. _____ Was adopted with Danny.

6. _____ Was the last child to be selected.

7. _____ Thinks she has always been the bad-luck penny.

8. _____ Wondered what he could ever do without Mike.

9. _____ Said that even the journal has a story in itself.

10. _____ Gave Frances a letter from her mother.

11. _____ Moved to Kansas to keep it a Free State.

12. _____ Hid under the corn fodder.

13. _____ Learned to milk a cow.

14. _____ Wrapped the cheese in a shawl.

15. _____ Felt there was nothing to do at Grandma's.

16. _____ Mike put out the fire on his shirt.

17. _____ Wrapped up a parcel with all her children's belongings.

18. _____ Rev. Brace's scout.

19. _____ Couldn't reach the gun in his satchel.

20. _____ Her ring meant a great deal to her.

21. _____ No one had called him a fine young man since his father died.

22. _____ Thought about applying for a Pony Express job.

23. _____ His pa never let him drive the wagon alone.

Answer Key

A Family Apart (*Worksheet, Chapters 1–6*)

Vocabulary

1. satchel	5. urchins	9. bounty	13. sentinels
2. destination	6. pamphlet	10. pickpocket	14. resentment
3. parcel	7. docked	11. idolized	15. accusation
4. pulverized	8. sepia	12. ornate	

Short Answer (Answers may vary.)

They can be thought of as men upholding the law of the land, or as men making a profit from the misery of slaves.

A Family Apart (*Worksheet, Chapters 7–13*)

Vocabulary

1. dollop	4. entitled	7. reputation	10. homespun
2. parlor	5. prominent	8. retrieve	11. valiant
3. spunk	6. valise	9. trestles	12. rebuked

Short Answer (Answers may vary.)

1. Frances learned that real sacrifice is loving someone enough to give up something you prize. Frances was willing to pay the price of her beliefs when she helped James and Odette. She gained a deeper understanding of her mother's sacrifice.

2. She told the Marshal that "Frankie" was a girl, and she arranged a reasonable story to explain the ownership of the shawl.

Final Test

Character Identification

1. Johnny	7. Megan	13. Frances	20. Katherine
2. Mr. and Mrs. Cummings	8. Danny	14. Frances	21. Mike
3. Janus and Odette	9. Grandma Briley	15. Jeff	22. Mike
4. Frances	10. Katherine	16. Mr. Crandon	23. Johnny
5. Peg	11. Mr. and Mrs. Cummings	17. Mrs. Kelly	
6. Mike	12. Janus and Odette	18. Andrew McNair	
		19. Captain Taylor	

Extension Activities

A Family Apart

Discussion

CHAPTER 1

1. So far, how do Jennifer and Jeff feel about this visit?

CHAPTER 2

1. Give examples from this chapter that show the reader how the upper-class people feel about the poor.
2. Why did Mother leave Ireland?
3. When did Frances feel she became an adult?

CHAPTER 3

1. Why is Mike angry with his father?
2. How does Mike steal from the man at the restaurant?
3. Why does Mike think he'll never get caught?

CHAPTER 4

1. Why does Mrs. Kelly give up her children?
2. What does Mrs. Kelly believe will happen to the children?
3. What promise does Frances make to her mother?

CHAPTER 5

1. Why does Frances decide to look like a boy?
2. How are the adoptive families described to the children?

CHAPTER 6

1. How does Frances react to Andrew?
2. What is the general attitude of the passengers concerning slavery?
3. Why do the children seem surprised about the animals?

CHAPTER 7

1. What is the reason Mr. Crandon gives for not liking Mike? What other reasons might there be?
2. How does Mike feel about the children being sent west for adoption?

CHAPTER 8

1. What is Captain Taylor's opinion of Mike?
2. Why does Frances seem confused about the word *sacrifice*?

CHAPTER 9

1. What does the reader know about Mike's new family?
2. What information does the reader get about the other children's new families?

CHAPTER 10

1. Why is Johnny glad to be "Frankie's" friend?
2. In what ways did "Frankie" almost give himself away?

CHAPTER 11

1. Why do you think the Marshal seems apologetic about his visit?
2. What is the Underground Railroad?

CHAPTER 12

1. Why did the Cummingses adopt Pete and "Frankie"?
2. Why did Janus and Odette finally run away from their master?

CHAPTER 13

1. What mistake did "Frankie" make?
2. How did Katherine know about Frances?

(continued)

A Family Apart (continued)

Reading

1. The other books in this Orphan Train Quartet series are:

   Caught in the Act
   In the Face of Danger
   A Place to Belong

2. Other books that depict prairie life during this time period are:

   Prairie Songs by Pam Conrad
   My Daniel by Pam Conrad
   The American Girls Collection—the *Kirsten* books by Janet Shaw
   Beyond the Divide by Joan Blos
   Honey Girl by Madge Harrah
   Save Queen of Sheba by Louise Moeri
   The Little House on the Prairie series by Laura Ingalls Wilder
   * *Sarah, Plain and Tall* by Patricia MacLachlan

   * covered in this volume

3. There are several good books for young adults that depict families set apart by economic circumstances. Here are some of them:

   * *Cave Under the City* by Harry Mazer
   Dicey's Song by Cynthia Voight
   The Journey of Natty Gann by Ann Matthews
   The Cookcamp by Gary Paulsen
   Lyddie by Katherine Paterson

   * covered in this volume

4. If students are intrigued by Frances's disguise as a boy, they might want to read the true-life adventures of Emma Edmonds, who not only dressed up as a male in order to enlist in the Union Army during the Civil War but became a spy. The book is *Behind Rebel Lines* by Seymour Reit.

Writing

1. The books in this series are based on Frances's imaginary journal. Imagine you are Frances's mother and think of her feelings after the children left. Write Mrs. Kelly's journal.

2. Andrew said that a committee of three prominent citizens approved each applicant for adoption. Try to imagine what those application forms must have been like. What kind of information would be needed? What questions should be asked?

(continued)

Research

Students interested in this time period could research:

(a) The famine in Ireland and Irish immigration to America

(b) The Orphan Train or the Children's Aid Society

(c) The Underground Railroad

(d) The first election of Abraham Lincoln

(e) The abolitionists and the pro-slavery point of view

Art

In Chapter 2 Frances stops to admire a doll in a shop window. An upper-class girl does the same. Research the period costumes (1860) of upper- and lower-class New Yorkers. Then illustrate the scene mentioned.

Drama

Rewrite and act out the scenes from Chapter 9 where the children are introduced to their adoptive families.

Video

There is a wonderful film called *Heaven on Earth* which tells the story of the "home children" sent to Canada between 1867 and 1914 because of hard economic times in England. Hearing about Canada, these British children thought they would be living in a place that was "heaven on earth." Unfortunately, life was hard and some home situations were cruel and demanding. It is a credit to the strength and courage of these children that at least 5% of Canada's population are descendants of the "home children." The film is 100 minutes long and was released for commercial purchase or rental in 1989. Since there is no rating, teacher review is highly recommended.

Number the Stars

by Lois Lowry

Synopsis

Nazi occupational soldiers are a resented but familiar sight in Annemarie's native Copenhagen. For the last three of her ten years, she has had to live with food shortages and rationed electricity. But she and her family cannot comply when the Germans decide to "relocate" the Danish Jews. Annemarie and her family bravely join resistance efforts to safeguard Denmark's Jews from Nazi tyranny.

Vocabulary

CHAPTER 1

1. stocky
2. hesitate
3. residential
4. skirted
5. contempt
6. hoodlums
7. anxiously
8. exaggerating
9. sabotage
10. impassive

Historical/ Geographical

- Resistance
- Copenhagen
- Nazis

CHAPTER 2

1. jubilee
2. crochet
3. trousseau
4. intricate
5. fiancé

Historical/ Geographical

- Hans Christian Andersen
- Amalienborg

- Christian X
- Denmark
- Norway
- Belgium
- France
- Sweden

CHAPTER 3

1. kroner
2. sarcastic
3. curfew
4. issued
5. tormenting
6. cocoon

Historical/ Geographical

- Jews
- Danes

CHAPTER 4

1. sophisticated
2. exasperated
3. stunned

Historical/ Geographical

- Tivoli Gardens
- Occupation
- Sabbath

- synagogue
- rabbi
- relocation

CHAPTER 5

1. intoned
2. harsh
3. winced

Historical/ Geographical

- Lutheran
- Star of David
- rationed
- blackout curtain

CHAPTER 6

1. suspicious
2. tentatively
3. reluctantly

Historical/ Geographical

- Klampenborg
- Gilleleje
- Baltic Sea
- Helsinger

CHPTER 7

1. gnarled
2. appliqued

CHAPTER 8

Historical/ Geographical

- military arrest
- custom

CHAPTER 9

1. affectionately
2. determined
3. hearse
4. mourning
5. urgency

CHAPTER 10

1. condescending
2. typhus

Historical/ Geographical

- psalm

CHAPTER 11

NONE

CHAPTER 12

1. route
2. horizon
3. imitating

CHAPTER 13

NONE

CHAPTER 14

1. latticed
2. vivid
3. tantalize

CHAPTER 15

1. insolent
2. contempt

CHAPTER 16

1. concealed

AFTERWORD

1. decency

Number the Stars—Chapters 1–7

Vocabulary: Fill in the blanks with appropriate vocabulary words taken from Chapters 1–7. Historical and geographical references may also be used. The chapter numbers are given in parentheses to aid you, if needed.

1. Some loyal Danish people secretly tried to (1) _____ the Nazis by damaging railroads and factories.

2. The Danes were proud of their own storyteller and author, (2) _____ .

3. The members of the (1) _____ were determined to bring harm to the Nazis any way they could.

4. Since the beginning of the Nazi (4) _____ of Denmark, coffee and tea were impossible to get.

5. It bothered Annemarie that although the Nazis had occupied (2) _____ for three years, they still couldn't speak the language.

6. To Annemarie it seemed there was a German soldier on every street corner in her city of (1) _____ .

7. Lise's (2) _____ was stored in a wooden trunk in Annemarie's bedroom.

8. Peter risked being out after (3) _____ to warn the family that the Germans had begun to close Jewish-run stores.

9. Annemarie was (4) _____ when she learned what Germans planned to do to the Jews.

10. The Nazis went to (4) _____ and took the names of all the Jewish people.

11. Annemarie (5) _____ when the soldier grabbed Ellen's hair.

12. Annemarie was being (3) _____ when she suggested that the Hirshe family went on vacation to the seashore.

13. Nazi (4) _____ really meant taking Jews to concentration camps and to their deaths.

14. Ellen's (5) _____ was the symbol of her faith.

15. Electricity had been (5) _____ since the Germans had occupied Denmark.

16. The German soldiers were (6) _____ of Ellen's dark hair.

17. Annemarie remembered when the soldier let his (5) _____ pose slip away a moment and had smiled at Kirsti.

18. Papa (6) _____ agreed to allow Mama and the girls to go alone on the trip.

Name: _____   Date: _____

Number the Stars—Chapter 8–Afterword

Crossword Puzzle: Use your knowledge of events throughout the book to complete the puzzle.

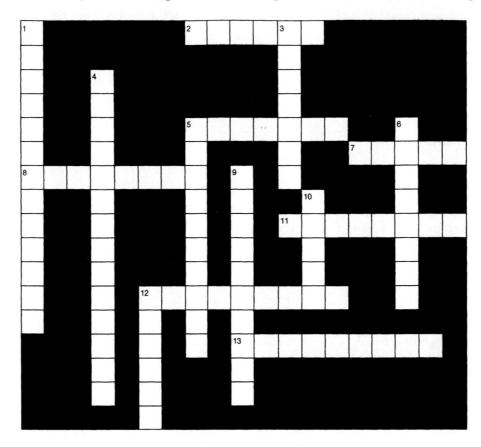

Down Clues

1. The German officer's voice was _____ when he said, "Poor Great-Aunt Birte."
3. There was a sense of _____ about Peter as he moved to assist in the escape.
4. Mama joked about butter being under _____ _____ by the German army.
5. Uncle Henrik knew Annemarie was _____ to help protect the Jews.
6. The path was _____ with thick tree roots hidden by leaves.
9. Annemarie _____ told the soldier that the German army eats all of Denmark's meat.
10. Annemarie traced the _____ in her mind and knew the path well.
12. In Denmark it is the _____ for dead relatives to be viewed by friends and family at home.

Across Clues

2. Mama told a brilliant lie about Aunt Birte dying of _____ .
5. This story of the _____ of the people of Denmark inspires us even today.
7. Peter knew the _____ by heart but still opened the Bible.
8. The soldier's voice was full of _____ when he said that her uncle had a pretty lunch.
11. When the Germans pushed into the house they saw only people _____ for Great-Aunt Birte.
12. The hiding places were carefully _____ in the fishing boats.
13. Annemarie liked to prolong the story's suspense in order to _____ her sister's curiosity.

Name: _____   Date: _____

Final Test
Number the Stars

Character Identification: Write the character's letter in the blank next to each description of that character. You may use a letter more than once.

(a) Nazi soldiers   (f) Papa
(b) Peter   (g) King Christian X
(c) Ellen   (h) Uncle Henrik
(d) Kirsti   (i) Mama
(e) Lise   (j) Annemarie

1. _____ Was run down by a German military car.
2. _____ Brought Mama and Papa the illegal newspaper, *The Free Danes*.
3. _____ Rode out every morning upon his horse, Jubilee.
4. _____ Had to wear "fish-shoes."
5. _____ Burned part of Tivoli Gardens to punish the Danish people.
6. _____ Her papa gave her the Star of David necklace when she was very small.
7. _____ Told Uncle Henrik he would be sending him "a carton of cigarettes."
8. _____ Said it is easier to be brave if you don't know everything.
9. _____ Promised to come back someday.
10. _____ Took lists of all the Jews from the synogogue.
11. _____ Offered to let the Germans see Great-Aunt Birte in her coffin.
12. _____ Drugged the baby.
13. _____ Pretended to be a very silly girl taking lunch to a fisherman.
14. _____ Used dogs to sniff out people who were hidden.
15. _____ Will wear her friend's necklace until she returns.

True/False: Write *true* or *false* for each of the following statements.

1. _____ Peter was buried next to Lise.
2. _____ Annemarie's mother told her all about the importance of the packet.
3. _____ The German soldier didn't want to look in the coffin because he thought it meant bad luck.
4. _____ The Jewish people were taken to Norway where they would be free.
5. _____ Ellen told the soldier that she was Lise.
6. _____ Neighbors helped to care for the homes of their missing Jewish friends.

Answer Key

Number the Stars (*Worksheet, Chapters 1–7*)

Vocabulary

1. sabotage
2. Hans Christian Andersen
3. Resistance
4. Occupation
5. Denmark
6. Copenhagen
7. trousseau
8. curfew
9. stunned
10. synagogue
11. winced
12. sarcastic
13. relocation
14. Star of David
15. rationed
16. suspicious
17. harsh
18. reluctantly

Number the Stars (*Worksheet, Chapters 8–Afterword*)

Crossword Puzzle

Word List
(for optional use with students)

contempt
concealed
condescending
custom
decency
determined
insolently
latticed
military arrest
mourning
psalm
route
tantalize
typhus
urgency

Final Test

Character Identification

1. e	4. d	7. f	10. a	13. j
2. b	5. a	8. h	11. i	14. a
3. g	6. c	9. c	12. b	15. j

True/False

1. false	3. false	5. true
2. false	4. false	6. true

Extension Activities

Number the Stars

Discussion

CHAPTER 1

1. Why do you think the Nazis had not bothered to learn the Danish language?

2. In what ways does the Danish Resistance try to hinder the Nazis in this first chapter?

CHAPTER 2

1. The Danes are very proud of their own Hans Christian Andersen. The author of this book, Lois Lowry, mentions that he wrote *The Little Mermaid*. Can you think of other stories he wrote?

2. How does the author let the reader know that Denmark's King Christian X is loved by his people?

CHAPTER 3

1. How does enforcing a curfew for the Danish people help the Nazi army?

2. Annemarie talks about the Danish people being bodyguards for King Christian X and the Jews. What does she mean?

CHAPTER 4

1. How did the Danes use their navy against the Nazis?

2. How did the Germans learn which citizens were Jews?

3. What do you think the Germans meant by "relocation"?

CHAPTER 5

1. In this chapter what brave thing did Annemarie do to "guard" Ellen from the German soldiers?

CHAPTER 6

1. What made Papa agree to allow Mama and the girls to go without him?

CHAPTER 7

1. Why does Mama want the girls to stay away from people while they are at Uncle Henrik's?

CHAPTER 8

1. What are some everyday things that Annemarie and her family have to do without during the war?

2. Why is Annemarie confused about the death in the family?

CHAPTER 9

1. Do you agree with Uncle Henrik that it is easier to be brave if one doesn't know everything?

CHAPTER 10

1. Why did the German officer refuse to see Great-Aunt Birte when Mama offered to open the casket?

2. Peter read a psalm about God who " . . . number the stars one by one." Why did the author title this book *Number the Stars*?

CHAPTER 11

1. What new form of pride could Annemarie see in the Rosen family as they waited to leave on the boat?

2. Why do you think Peter drugged the baby?

(continued)

Number the Stars (continued)

CHAPTER 12

1. Annemarie thought of Papa waiting and wondering at home. Why does she think it would be difficult for him there?

CHAPTER 13

1. What is Annemarie's "cover" as she goes to deliver the packet to Uncle Henrik?

CHAPTER 14

1. What children's story does Annemarie think of as she goes into the forest? Why is it ironic?

CHAPTER 15

1. What was in the packet?
2. How did the dogs react to it?

CHAPTER 16

1. Explain Uncle Henrik's definition of "brave."

2. What clues are given in this book to let the reader know that Peter is a member of the Resistance?

3. Why was the packet Annemarie gave Uncle Henrik important?

CHAPTER 17

1. What did neighbors and friends do for the homes of the Jewish people? Why?
2. How did Peter die?
3. Why do you think it is important to Annemarie to wear Ellen's necklace?

AFTERWORD

1. Discuss the historical facts on which this story is based.
2. In what ways did the people of Denmark exemplify human decency?

Reading

1. Suggested books concerning the Holocaust for this age group are:

   Escape From Warsaw by Ian Serraillier * *The Devil's Arithmetic* by Jane Yolen
   The Upstairs Room by Johanna Reiss   *The Diary of Anne Frank*

   * covered in this volume

2. Other books written by Lois Lowry include:

Anastasia Krupnik (and the other *Anastasia* books)	*The One Hundredth Thing About Caroline*
Rabble Starkey	*Us and Uncle Fraud*
Taking Care of Terrific	*All About Sam*
Autumn Street	*A Summer to Die*
Switcharound	*Find A Stranger, Say Goodbye*

3. Biographies about Hans Christian Andersen or King Christian X of Denmark might provide an interesting study of background for the book.

(continued)

Writing

Students may enjoy writing activities such as:

Sequels—Write about the things that will stay the same and the things that will change when Ellen and her family return to Denmark.

Articles—Chronicle the major events in this book by writing them in article form for the newspaper *The Free Danes*.

Letters—If Ellen and Annemarie could have exchanged letters after Ellen left Denmark, what would those letters say?

Research—Students interested in history could research information on the following subjects:

- The Nazi "relocation" of Jews during World War II
- King Christian X of Denmark
- Sweden's neutrality during World War II
- Resistance fighters during World War II
- Thor, god of Thunder, in Scandanavian mythology
- The Star of David
- The Holocaust
- Hans Christian Andersen
- Typhus
- Norway's efforts to resist German takeover in World War II
- The Danes' decision to sink their navy during World War II

Art

1. Draw maps of Denmark, the Scandanavian countries, and landmarks mentioned in this book. (Areas of geographical interest are specified in the vocabulary.)
2. Recreate or illustrate the following scenes:
   - The funeral for Great-Aunt Birte
   - The soldiers at Uncle Henrik's boat with the people hidden in the secret compartment
   - The German soldiers suspicious of Ellen in Annemarie's room

Drama

Rewrite in play form and act out one of the scenes listed above in the Art section.

APPENDIX

Bibliography by Thematic Units

Books with Athletic Heroes

* Starred books are covered in the *Best Young Adult Novels* series.

The Boy Who Drank Too Much	Shep Greene	Hockey
Brian Piccolo: A Short Season	Jeannie Morris	Football
Brian's Song	William Blinn	Football
The Contender	Robert Lipsyte	Boxing
*Half the Battle	Lynn Hall	Horse Racing
Hoops	Walter Dean Myers	Basketball
The Karate Kid	B. B. Hiller	Karate
The Moves Make the Man	Bruce Brooks	Basketball
*No Dragons to Slay	Jan Greenberg	Soccer
The Runner	Cynthia Voigt	Track
Something for Joey	Richard E. Peck	Football
S.O.R. Losers	Avi	Soccer
Tell Me If the Lovers Are Losers	Cynthia Voigt	Volleyball
Winning	Robin Brancato	Football
Zamboomer	R. R. Knudsen	Baseball

Decisions and Consequences

* Starred books are covered in the *Best Young Adult Novels* series.

About David	Susan Beth Pfeffer
After the First Death	Robert Cormier
Beyond the Chocolate War	Robert Cormier
Bless the Beasts and Children	Glendon Swarthout
Blinded by the Light	Robin Brancato
The Boll Weevil Express	P. J. Petersen
Born Free	Joy Adamson
*Bridge to Terabithia	Katherine Paterson
Call of the Wild	Jack London
Caribou	Meg Wolitzer
The Children's Story	James Clavell
The Chocolate War	Robert Cormier
*A Day No Pigs Would Die	Robert Newton Peck

The Day They Came to Arrest the Book	Nat Hentoff
Devil's Race	Avi
The Disappearance	Rosa Guy
Edgar Allen	John Neufeld
The Elephant Tree	Harriet Luger
Everything But Tuesdays and Sundays	Peter Filichia
Gentlehands	M. E. Kerr
Go Ask Alice	Anonymous
Goodbye to Good Ol' Charlie	P. J. Petersen
The Gorilla Signs Love	Barbara Brenner
Hatter Fox	Marilyn Harris
Here's to the Sophomores	P. J. Petersen
I Am the Cheese	Robert Cormier
I Know What You Did Last Summer	Lois Duncan
In the Shadow of the Wind	Luke Wallin
Julie of the Wolves	Jean Craighead George
Killing Mr. Griffin	Lois Duncan
The Lost Mission	Harry Mazer
Laughing Boy	Oliver La Farge
The Light in the Forest	Conrad Richter
A Little Love	Virginia Hamilton
Lord of the Flies	William Golding
Mr. and Mrs. Bo Jo Jones	Ann Head
My Darling, My Hamburger	Paul Zindel
My Shadow Ran Fast	Bill Sands
Night Kites	M. E. Kerr
Nobody Else Can Walk It for You	P. J. Petersen
On My Honor	Marion Dane Bauer
The Outsiders	S. E. Hinton
Phoebe	Patricia Dizenzo
The Pigman	Paul Zindel
The Pigman's Legacy	Paul Zindel
Rumble Fish	S. E. Hinton
Secrets of the Shopping Mall	Richard Peck
Sharelle	John Neufeld
Snow Bound	Harry Mazer
Steffie Can't Come Out to Play	Fran Arrick
Summer Snow	Marilyn Levy
That Was Then, This Is Now	S. E. Hinton
Tunnel Vision	Fran Arrick
Up in Seth's Room	Norma Fox Mazer
The Wave	Morton Rhue
Would You Settle for Improbable?	P. J. Petersen

Dreams and Goals

* Starred books are covered in the *Best Young Adult Novels* series.

Anne of Green Gables	L. M. Montgomery
*Bridge to Terabithia	Katherine Paterson
*The Cave Under the City	Harry Mazer
Christy	Catherine Marshall
*The Fighting Ground	Avi
Fingers	William Sleator
*The Girl Who Owned a City	O. T. Nelson
The Giver	Lynn Hall
Goodbye to Good Ol' Charlie	P. J. Petersen
*Homecoming	Cynthia Voigt
Hot Rod	Henry Gregor Felsen
*The Last Mission	Harry Mazer
A Little Love	Virginia Hamilton
*Motown and Didi	Walter Dean Myers
One Way to Ansonia	Judie Angell
*Rebels of the Heavenly Kingdom	Katherine Paterson
Shadi	Margaret Embry
*Sharelle	John Neufeld
*Steffie Can't Come Out to Play	Fran Arrick
*Teacup Full of Roses	Sharon Bell Mathis
*Where the Red Fern Grows	Wilson Rawls

Growing Up

* Starred books are covered in the *Best Young Adult Novels* series.

*A Day No Pigs Would Die	Robert Newton Peck
*Are You There God? It's Me, Margaret	Judy Blume
Bless Me, Ultima	Rudolfo A. Anaya
Eight Plus One: Stories by Robert Cormieer	Robert Cormier
The Everlasting Hills	Irene Hunt
I Never Loved Your Mind	Paul Zindel
James at 15	April Smith
Joy in the Morning	Betty Smith
Los Alamos Light	Larry Bograd
Mom, the Wolf Man and Me	Norma Klein

*The Sign of the Beaver   Elizabeth George Speare
Pardon Me, You're Stepping on My   Paul Zindel
    Eyeball!
Rascal   Sterling North
Red Sky at Morning   Richard Bradford
Seventeenth Summer   Maureen Daly
Shane   Jack Schaefer
*No Place for Me   Barthe DeClements
*Sounder   William Armstrong
Summer of My German Soldier   Bette Greene
Tell Me If the Lovers Are Losers   Cynthia Voigt
To Kill a Mockingbird   Harper Lee
Up A Road Slowly   Irene Hunt
*Walk Through Cold Fire   Cin Forshay-Lunsford
Wart, Son of Toad   Alden R. Carter
Water Girl   Joyce Carol Thomas
When the Legends Die   Hal Borland
William   Irene Hunt

Family Problems

* Starred books are covered in the *Best Young Adult Novels* series.

About David   Susan Beth Pfeffer
*Are You in the House Alone?   Richard Peck
*The Best Little Girl in the World   Steven Levenkron
The Boll Weevil Express   P. J. Petersen
*The Boy Who Drank Too Much   Shep Greene
The Divorce Express   Paula Danzinger
The Everlasting Hills   Irene Hunt
Family Secrets   Norma Klein
A Gift of Magic   Lois Duncan
God's Radar   Fran Arrick
*Homecoming   Cynthia Voigt
Jacob Have I Loved   Katherine Paterson
The Jellyfish Season   Mary Downing Hahn
*Lindsay, Lindsay, Fly Away Home   Stella Pevsner
Lisa, Bright and Dark   John Neufeld
*The Lottery Rose   Irene Hunt
*Motown and Didi   Walter Dean Myers
*My Darling, My Hamburger   Paul Zindel
*Night Kites   M. E. Kerr

Ordinary People	Judith Guest
*Park's Quest	Katherine Paterson
*The Pigman	Paul Zindel
*The Pinballs	Betsy Byars
The Runner	Cynthia Voigt
*Sarah, Plain and Tall	Patricia MacLachlan
*Sharelle	John Neufeld
*A Solitary Blue	Cynthia Voigt
*Sounder	William Armstrong
*Summer Snow	Marilyn Levy
*Teacup Full of Roses	Sharon Bell Mathis
Tex	S. E. Hinton
*Tiger Eyes	Judy Blume
*Tunnel Vision	Fran Arrick

Fantasy

* Starred books are covered in the *Best Young Adult Novels* series.

Among the Dolls	William Sleator
Behind the Attic Wall	Sylvia Cassedy
Beowulf, a Retelling	Robert Nye
The Crystal Cave	Mary Stewart
Dragondrums	Anne McCaffrey
Dragonsinger	Anne McCaffrey
Dragonsong	Anne McCaffrey
The Dreadful Future of Blossom Culp	Richard Peck
The Farthest Shore	Ursula Le Guin
The Fellowship of the Ring	J. R. R. Tolkien
The Grey King	Susan Cooper
Hangin' Out with Cici	Francine Pascal
The Hobbit	J. R. R. Tolkien
Iseult	Dee Morrison Meaney
The Lion, the Witch and the Wardrobe	C. S. Lewis
Locked in Time	Lois Duncan
The Night Walkers	Otto Coontz
The Once and Future King	T. H. White
*The Phantom Tollbooth	Norton Juster
Playing Beattie Bow	Ruth Parks
Portrait of Jenny	Robert Nathan
The Return of the King	J. R. R. Tolkien
The Silver Citadel	Anthony Horowitz

Something Wicked This Way Comes	Ray Bradbury
*Stranger with My Face	Lois Duncan
A Swiftly Tilting Planet	Madeleine L'Engle
Tombs of Atuan	Ursula Le Guin
*Tuck Everlasting	Natalie Babbitt
The Two Towers	J. R. R. Tolkien
Unicorns in the Rain	Barbara Cohen
The Watcher in the Woods	Florence Engel Randal
Watership Down	Richard Adams
A Wind in the Door	Madeleine L'Engle
A Wizard of Earthsea	Ursula Le Guin
*A Wrinkle in Time	Madeleine L'Engle

Historical Novels

* Starred books are covered in the *Best Young Adult Novels* series.

*Across Five Aprils	Irene Hunt	Civil War
April Morning	Howard Fast	Revolutionary War
*The Cave Under the City	Harry Mazer	The Depression
Ceremony of Innocence	James Forman	World War II
*The Devil's Arithmetic	Jane Yolen	The Holocaust
*A Family Apart	Joan Lowery Nixon	1860's Orphan Train
Farewell to Manzanar	Jeanne Wakatsuda Houston	World War II
*The Fighting Ground	Avi	Revolutionary War
A Gathering of Days	Joan Blos	New England, 1830–32
The Hiding Place	Corrie Ten Boom	World War II
Johnny Tremain	Esther Forbes	Revolutionary War
The Journey of Natty Gann	Ann Matthews	The Depression
*The Last Mission	Harry Mazer	World War II
Mrs. Mike	Benedict and Nancy Freedman	Canada, early 1900's
My Brother Sam Is Dead	James and Christopher Collier	Revolutionary War
*No Promises in the Wind	Irene Hunt	The Depression
*Number the Stars	Lois Lowry	World War II
*Rebels of the Heavenly Kingdom	Katherine Paterson	Chinese Revolution
Streams to the River, River to the Sea	Scott O'Dell	Sacajawea
The Witch of Blackbird Pond	Elizabeth George Speare	Puritans

Humorous

The Alfred G. Graebner Memorial High School Handbook of Rules and Regulations: A Novel	Ellen Conford
Can You Sue Your Parents for Malpractice?	Paula Danzinger
The Cat Ate My Gym Suit	Paula Danzinger
Do Black Patent Shoes Really Reflect Up?	John R. Powers
The Dog Who Wouldn't Be	Farley Mowat
Goodbye to Good Ol' Charlie	P. J. Petersen
Hangin' Out with Cici	Francine Pascal
Seven Days to a Brand New Me	Ellen Conford

Animals

* Starred books are covered in the *Best Young Adult Novels* series.

All Creatures Great and Small	James Herriott
All Things Bright and Beautiful	James Herriott
All Things Wise and Wonderful	James Herriott
Call of the Wild	Jack London
The Dog Who Wouldn't Be	Farley Mowat
The Incredible Journey	Sheila Burnford
National Velvet	Enid Bagnold
Never Cry Wolf	Farley Mowat
Rascal	Sterling North
Summer of the Monkeys	Wilson Rawls
Where the Red Fern Grows	Wilson Rawls

Mysteries

* Starred books are covered in the *Best Young Adult Novels* series.

The Birthday Murderer	Jay Bennett
The Callender Papers	Cynthia Voigt

The Dangling Witness	Jay Bennett
Daughters of Eve	Lois Duncan
A Deadly Game of Magic	Joan Lowery Nixon
The Death Ticket	Jay Bennett
*Deathwatch	Robb White
Devil's Race	Avi
*The Dollhouse Murders	Betty Ren Wright
Down a Dark Hall	Lois Duncan
*The Executioner	Jay Bennett
*From the Mixed-Up Files of Mrs. Basil E. Frankweiler	E. L. Konigsburg
*A Gift of Magic	Lois Duncan
*I Know What You Did Last Summer	Lois Duncan
*The Indian in the Cupboard	Lynne Reid Banks
*Killing Mr. Griffin	Lois Duncan
Locked in Time	Lois Duncan
The Other Side of Dark	Joan Lowery Nixon
Ransom	Lois Duncan
*The Sandman's Eyes	Patricia Windsor
*The Seance	Joan Lowery Nixon
Secrets of the Shopping Mall	Richard Peck
The Stalker	Joan Lowery Nixon
*Stranger with My Face	Lois Duncan
Summer of Fear	Lois Duncan
They Never Came Home	Lois Duncan
*The Third Eye	Lois Duncan
The Westing Game	Ellen Raskin
What Eric Knew	James Howe
Wolf Rider	Avi

Nonfiction

The Acorn People	Ron Jones	Autobiography
And No Birds Sang	Farley Mowat	World War II
Anne Frank: Diary of a Young Girl	Anne Frank	World War II
The Boat Who Wouldn't Float	Farley Mowat	Adventure
Brian Piccolo: A Short Season	Jeannie Morris	Biography
Dibs, In Search of Self	Virginia Axline	Mental Illness
Dove	Robin Graham and L. T. Derek	Sailing
Farewell to Manzanar	Jeanne Wakatsuda Houston	World War II
Hiroshima	John Hersey	World War II
I Am Fifteen—and I Don't Want to Die	Christine Arnothy	World War II
I Know Why the Caged Bird Sings	Maya Angelou	Autobiography
My Shadow Ran Fast	Bill Sands	Autobiography
Never Cry Wolf	Farley Mowat	Wildlife Study
A Night to Remember	Walter Lord	Titanic Sinking
Robyn's Book	Robyn Miller	Cystic Fibrosis
A Shining Season	William Buchanan	Biography
Somebody Else's Kids	Torey Hayden	Mental Illness
Something for Joey	Richard E. Peck	Leukemia/Sports
A Walk Across America	Peter Jenkins	Adventure
The Walk West	Barbara and Peter Jenkins	Adventure

Science Fiction

* Starred books are covered in the *Best Young Adult Novels* series.

Among the Dolls	William Sleator
The Boy Who Reversed Himself	William Sleator
Fahrenheit 451	Ray Bradbury
Fingers	William Sleator
*The Girl Who Owned a City	O. T. Nelson
*The Green Book	Jill Paton Walsh
*Interstellar Pig	William Sleator
*Into the Dream	William Sleator
Lucifer's Hammer	Larry Niven and Jerry Pournelle
The Martian Chronicles	Ray Bradbury
Singularity	William Sleator
Stranger in a Strange Land	Robert Heinlein
2001: A Space Odyssey	Arthur C. Clarke
*Z for Zachariah	Robert C. O'Brien

Social/School Problems

* Starred books are covered in the *Best Young Adult Novels* series.

The Alfred G. Graebner Memorial High School Handbook of Rules and Regulations: A Novel	Ellen Conford
The Chocolate War	Robert Cormier
The Day They Came to Arrest the Book	Nat Hentoff
*Deenie	Judy Blume
The Giver	Lynn Hall
Goodbye to Good Ol' Charlie	P. J. Petersen
Here's to the Sophomores	P. J. Petersen
If It's Not Funny, Why Am I Laughing?	Philippa Green Mulford
*Izzy, Willy-Nilly	Cynthia Voigt
The Language of Goldfish	Zibby O'Neal
*Lindsay, Lindsay, Fly Away Home	Stella Pevsner
*The Pinballs	Betsy Byars
Pretty in Pink	H. B. Gilmour
Seven Days to a Brand New Me	Ellen Conford
*Sharelle	John Neufeld
S.O.R. Losers	Avi
*Summer Snow	Marilyn Levy
*Would You Settle for Improbable?	P. J. Petersen

Special Challenges

* Starred books are covered in the *Best Young Adult Novels* series.

The Acorn People	Ron Jones	Physical Disabilities
Alas, Babylon	Pat Frank	Wartime Survival
*Are You in the House Alone?	Richard Peck	Rape
*The Best Little Girl in the World	Steven Levenkron	Anorexia
Black Like Me	John Howard Griffin	Racism
*The Boy Who Drank Too Much	Shep Greene	Alcoholism
*The Bumblebee Flies Anyway	Robert Cormier	Death
Captives in a Foreign Land	Susan Lowry Rardin	Kidnapping
Clunie	Robert Newton Peck	Mental Retardation
The Contender	Robert Lipsyte	Drug Abuse
*The Creep	Susan Dodson	Child Abuse

*The Crossing	Gary Paulsen	Illegal Aliens
Dead Birds Singing	Marc Talbert	Death
*Deenie	Judy Blume	Physical Disability
*The Elephant Tree	Harriet Luger	Survival
Eric	Doris Lund	Death
Friends Till the End	Todd Strasser	Death
God's Radar	Fran Arrick	Religious Rebirth
*Half the Battle	Lynn Hall	Blindness
*Hatchet	Gary Paulsen	Wilderness Survival
*Hatter Fox	Marilyn Harris	Juvenile Delinquency
Hey, Dummy	Kin Platt	Mental Retardation
I Am Fifteen—and I Don't Want to Die	Christine Arnothy	Wartime Survival
I Never Promised You a Rose Garden	Joanne Greenberg	Mental Illness
*Izzy, Willy-Nilly	Cynthia Voigt	Physical Disability
*Julie of the Wolves	Jean C. George	Survival
The Language of Goldfish	Zibby O'Neal	Suicide
The Late Great Me	Sandra Scoppettone	Alcoholism
Light a Single Candle	Beverly Butler	Blindness
Lisa, Bright and Dark	John Neufeld	Mental Illness
*The Lottery Rose	Irene Hunt	Child Abuse
My Name Is Davy and I'm an Alcoholic	Anne Snyder	Alcoholism
*Night Kites	M. E. Kerr	AIDS
*A Night Without Stars	James Howe	Physical Deformity
*No Dragons to Slay	Jan Greenberg	Cancer
Robyn's Book	Robyn Miller	Cystic Fibrosis
*Sharelle	John Neufeld	Pregnancy
*Snow Bound	Harry Mazer	Survival
*Summer to Die	Lois Lowry	Death
Winning	Robin Brancato	Physical Disability

Special Relationships

* Starred books are covered in the *Best Young Adult Novels* series.

Born Free	Joy Adamson
*Bridge to Terabithia	Katherine Paterson
*The Bumblebee Flies Anyway	Robert Cormier
*The Cave Under the City	Harry Mazer
Edgar Allen	John Neufeld

The Everlasting Hills	Irene Hunt
Fast Sam, Cool Clyde, and Stuff	Walter Dean Myers
The Giver	Lynn Hall
*The Gorilla Signs Love	Barbara Brenner
Hangin' Out with Cici	Francine Pascal
*The Lottery Rose	Irene Hunt
*The Outsiders	S. E. Hinton
*The Pigman	Paul Zindel
The Pigman's Legacy	Paul Zindel
*The Pinballs	Betsy Byars
Rascal	Sterling North
The Silver Citadel	Anthony Horowitz
*Snow Bound	Harry Mazer
Summer of My German Soldier	Bette Greene
Tex	S. E. Hinton
That Was Then, This Is Now	S. E. Hinton
*Walk Through Cold Fire	Cin Forshay-Lunsford
*Where the Red Fern Grows	Wilson Rawls
*Z for Zachariah	Robert C. O'Brien

Classics and Young Adult Literature

The books on the left are considered "classics." The titles on the right are high-quality young adult books that deal with the same themes as the classics. When students read the more manageable young adult books they will understand the theme, and more readily move toward the classics (or better understand the classics) when they encounter them in the classroom.

*Starred books are covered in the *Best Young Adult Novels* series.

1. Jane Eyre

by Charlotte Brontë

Eager to be competent in her new role as a governess, Jane Eyre becomes surrounded in mystery and haunted by wild cries in her new house.

Down a Dark Hall

by Lois Duncan

Sent to a private girls' school, Kit soon finds out that the girls' minds are being used and the whole school is shrouded in mystery.

2. The Good Earth

by Pearl Buck

A Chinese peasant and his family survive through famine, drought, and revolution as he pursues his dream to own land.

Mrs. Mike

by Benedict and Nancy Freedman

Based on the true story of Katherine Flannigan, the book shows her life from the age of 16 when she marries a Canadian Mountie and learns to love and hate the rugged North.

3. Lord Jim

by Joseph Conrad

Jim, the protagonist of the story, makes a tragic error that affects him for the rest of his life.

*I Know What You Did Last Summer

by Lois Duncan

Four teenagers accidentally kill a young boy on a bicycle. They silently live with their guilt until a year later when someone starts to get revenge.

4. Robinson Crusoe

by Daniel Defoe

A man is shipwrecked and finds refuge on an uninhabited island. This tale shows his survival techniques that turn his island into a comfortable home.

*Deathwatch

by Robb White

In the desert with no clothes, food, or water and hunted by a madman with a .357 Magnum, young Ben tries to survive, using his knowledge of the desert and his own determination.

*Snow Bound

by Harry Mazer

Lost in a blizzard in upper New York State, teenagers Tony and Cindy have to learn how to help each other in order to survive.

5. One Flew Over the Cuckoo's Nest

by Ken Kesey

A rebel in a mental hospital leads his fellow inmates in a revolt against the head nurse and the hospital rules.

*The Bumblebee Flies Anyway

by Robert Cormier

Sixteen-year-old Barney has a confident manner, being the control subject in an experimental hospital for the terminally ill. However, as he comes to care for some of the other patients, he realizes the sobering truth about himself.

6. A Separate Peace

by John Knowles

Finny and Gene are best friends even as Gene comes to grips with his own jealousy and hatred of Finny. Set in a New England boys' school in the 1940's, the tensions building up into World War II are reflected in the tensions of the young men.

*Half the Battle

by Lynn Hall

A young blind boy is determined to be part of an endurance race on horseback. With the help of his brother, he trains and competes, only to discover the deep-seated jealousy his brother has always felt for him.

Jacob Have I Loved

by Katherine Paterson

Sara Louise has always been jealous of her beautiful twin sister. Set on an island off the New England coast, the novel shows how Sara learns to live with her sibling rivalry.

7. *Of Mice and Men*

by John Steinbeck

A migrant worker tries to protect his friend, a retarded man, until even he cannot stop an accidental killing.

Clunie

by Robert Newton Peck

A retarded high school girl only has one friend, and even his friendship cannot stop her from a rape and her premature death.

Hey, Dummy

by Kin Platt

What happens when a boy befriends a brain-damaged kid is the basis for this story.

8. *The Grapes of Wrath*

by John Steinbeck

The whole era of the Depression is shown in one family's move to the West. The Joads continue to struggle in their quest for a better life.

The Journey of Natty Gann

by Ann Matthews

During the Depression, Natty travels across America, jumping trains, in order to find her father.

9. *Steppenwolf*

by Hermann Hesse

A man of 50 considers himself two separate personalities: a man and a wolf.

Lisa, Bright and Dark

by John Neufeld

A teenage girl confronts her schizophrenia and lets her friends "counsel" her until she can obtain professional help.

10. *Lord of the Flies*

by William Golding

Innocence ends very quickly when a group of British boys are abandoned on an island and must set up their own society, with violence taking a major role.

The Chocolate War

by Robert Cormier

A simple fund-raising drive selling chocolates draws some of the leaders of a school into ruthless acts of violence, against the school and against each other.

The Girl Who Owned a City

by O. T. Nelson

A plague wipes out all adults, and one girl takes the lead in organizing a new community.

11. *Oliver Twist*

by Charles Dickens

In Victorian England, a poor abandoned child emerges into a confident and loved boy.

The Lottery Rose

by Irene Hunt

Beaten by his mother's boyfriend, ostracized by his teacher, and neglected by his mother, seven-year-old Georgie mends slowly in a boys' school where he learns to love again.

12. Dracula

by Bram Stoker

Count Dracula's habits of taking innocent young women and turning then into vampires is finally stopped by three brave Englishmen.

The Night Walkers

by Otto Coontz

Something is changing all of the people in town into night creatures who prey on the innocent. Only one teenage girl understands what is happening and tries to warn the otheers.

13. The Bell Jar

by Sylvia Plath

Later taking her own life, the author tells a story of a young woman so confused and depressed by her life that she commits suicide.

*Tunnel Vision

by Fran Arrick

Leaving no note or explanation, a young teenage boy commits suicide, leaving his friends, family, and girlfriend to wonder why.

14. To Kill a Mockingbird

by Harper Lee

Growing up in a prejudiced southern town during the Depression, a young girl tells how her lawyer father defends a black man against a rape charge.

*Sounder

by William Armstrong

A young boy learns about racial injustice and how to become a man in the South in the early 1900's.

15. Catch-22

by Joseph Heller

Men deal with their frustrations during World War II in this sometimes crazy, sometimes sickening book about American soldiers in Italy.

*The Last Mission

by Harry Mazer

A 15-year-old boy lies about his age and becomes a bomber for the U.S. Army Air Force of World War II. Rather than finding war an exciting, glorious adventure, he has to face the truth.

Additional Professional Reading

Barr, Helen. "I Saw the Movie, But I Couldn't Read the Book." *Journal of Reading*, March 1986, pp. 511-515.

Baumann, James F. "Implications for Reading Instruction from the Research on Teacher and School Effectiveness." *Journal of Reading*, November 1984, pp. 109-115.

Becoming a Nation of Readers. The National Institute of Education, 1984.

Fort, Jerry. "Young Adult Literature: A Valuable Source of the Classroom." *The New Mexico Journal of Reading*, Spring 1986, pp. 15-17.

Frick, Hollee A. "The Value of Sharing Stories Orally with Middle Grade Students." *Journal of Reading*, January 1986, pp. 300-303.

Goodman, Yetta. "A Reading Program to Live With: Focus on Comprehension." *Language Arts*, Nov/Dec 1977, pp. 868-879.

Reed, Arthea J. S. *Reaching Adolescents—The Young Adult Book and the School*. Holt, Rinehart and Winston, New York, 1985.

Rupe, Mary, and Patricia Tarry-Stevens. "Employing a Novel Approach." *The New Mexico Journal of Reading*, Winter 1988, pp. 19-22.